Table of Contents

Garden Counting Fun

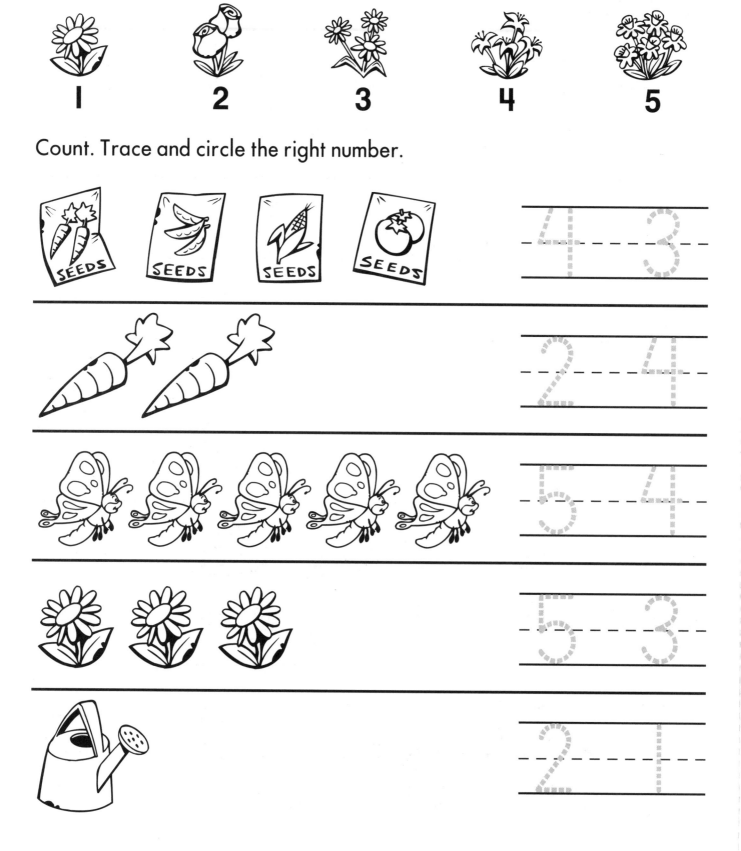

1   2   3   4   5

Count. Trace and circle the right number.

4   3

2   4

5   4

5   3

2   1

Counting objects and tracing numerals 1–5

How Many Friends?

Count. Write how many.

Have a Ball

Count. Write how many.

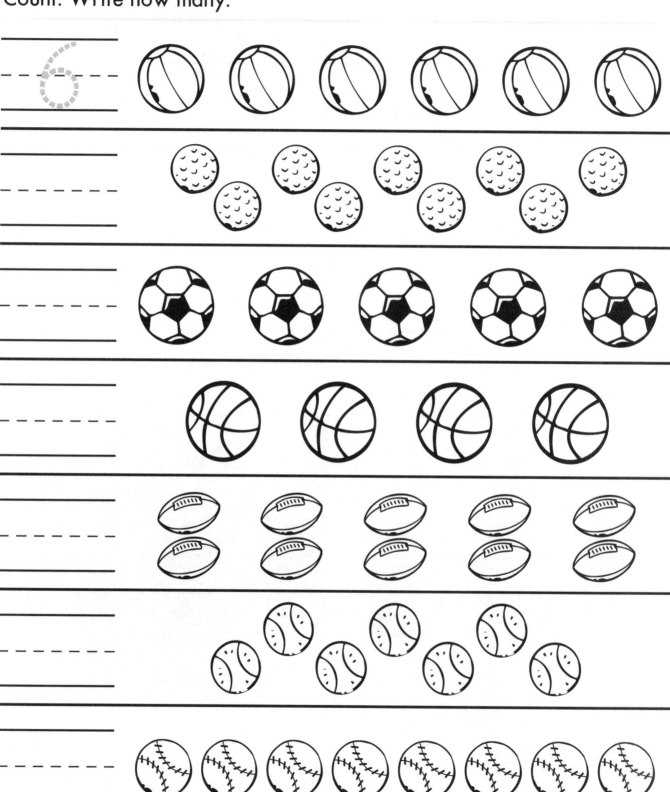

Counting objects and writing numerals to 10

1 to 10, Then 10 to 1

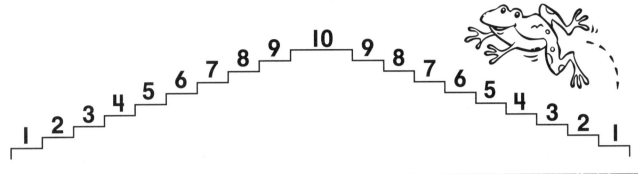

Write 1 to 10.

Write 10 to 1.

Count up the ladder and color the spaces that show the numbers 2, 4, 6, and 8.

Look Up High

Count. Write how many.

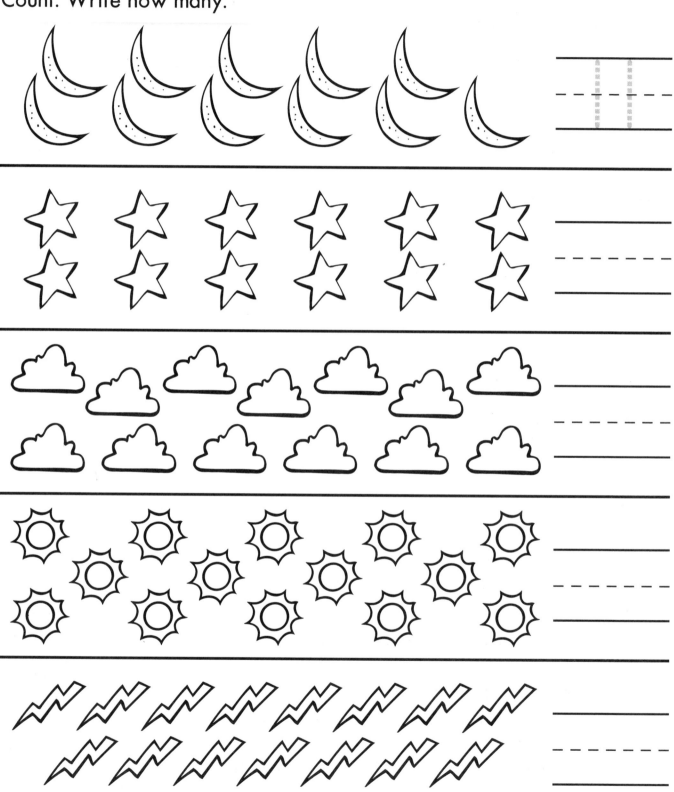

Counting objects and writing numerals 11–15

Fruity Snacks

Trace the number in each box. Draw lines to match.

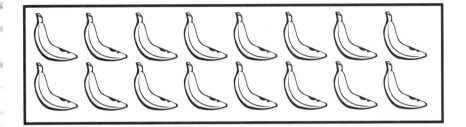

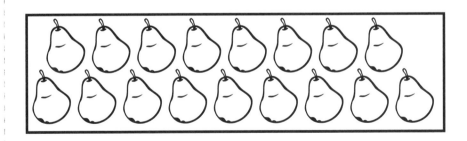

School Supplies

Count. Write how many.

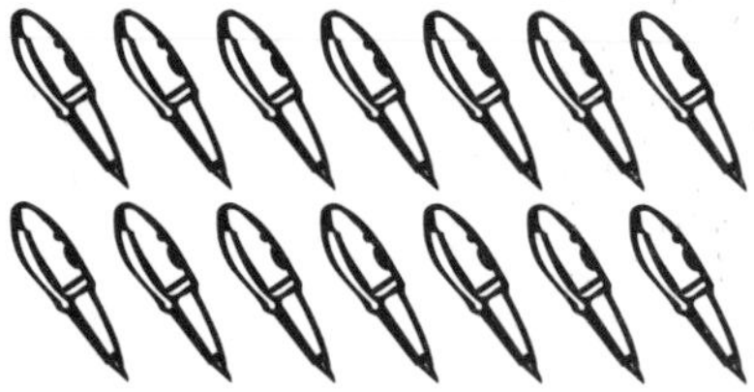

_14_

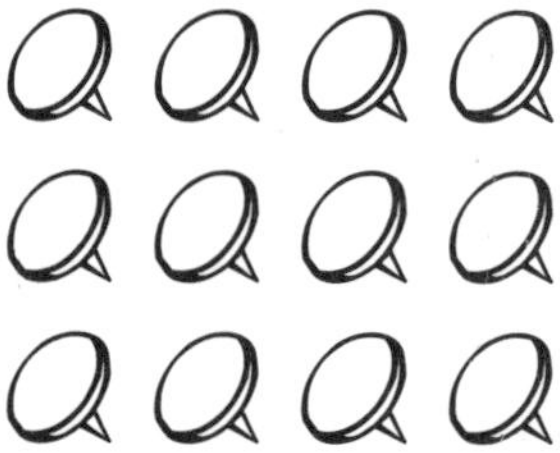

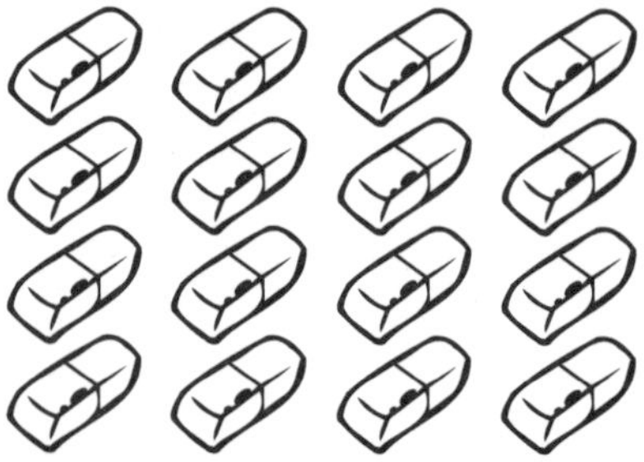

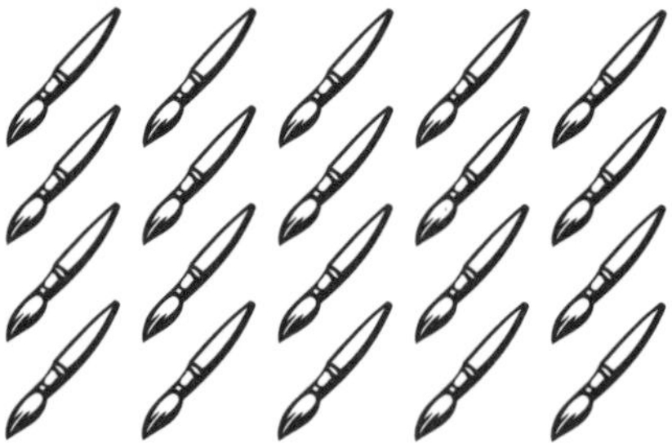

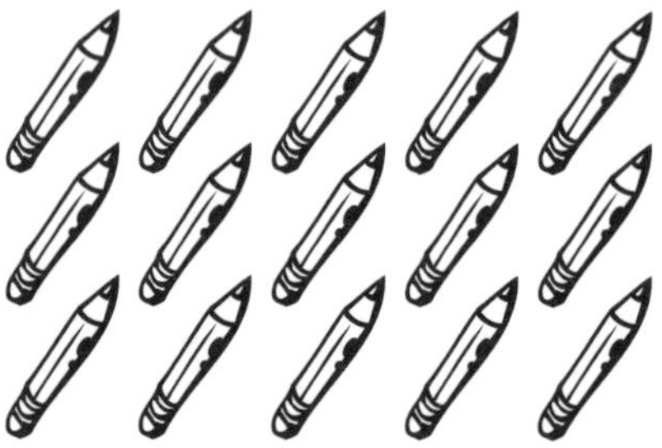

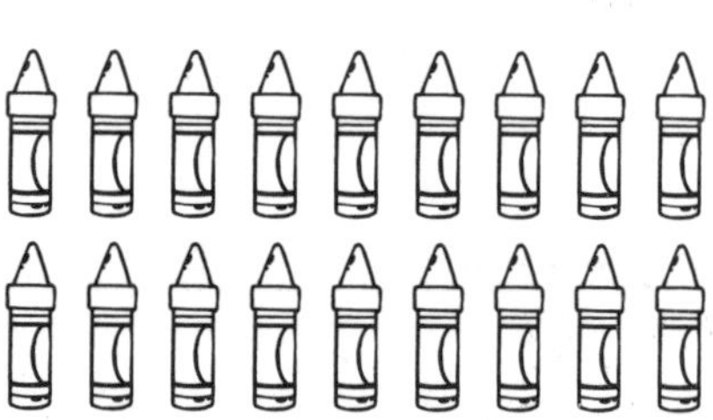

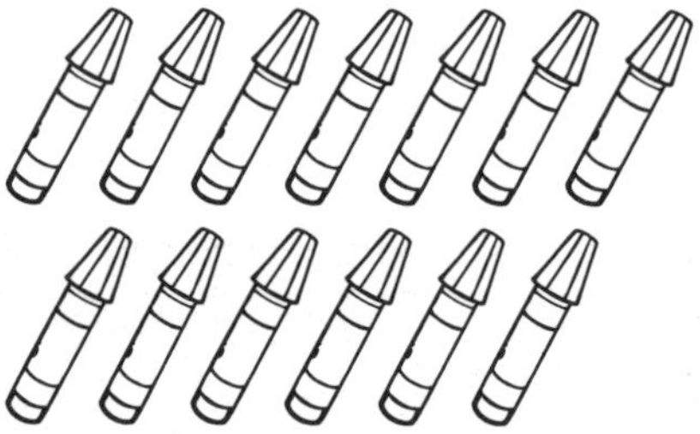

_____

_____

_____

_____

_____

_____

_____

_____

_____

Counting and writing numerals to 20

All Numbers Aboard!

Write 1 to 20.

Dot's Great!

Connect the dots from 1 to 20. Color the picture.

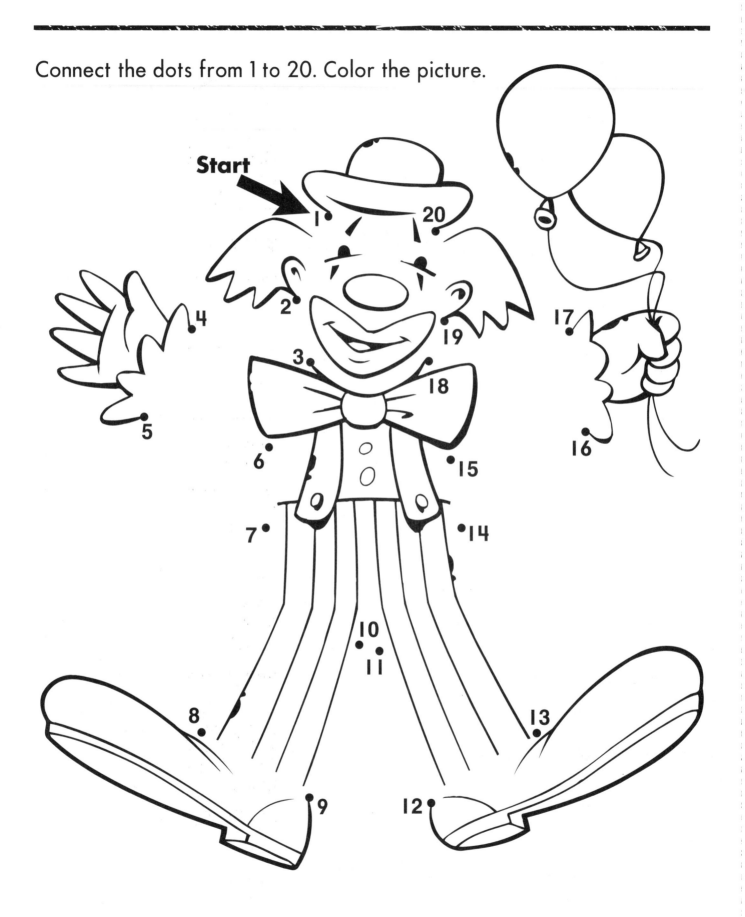

Start

Counting by 2's

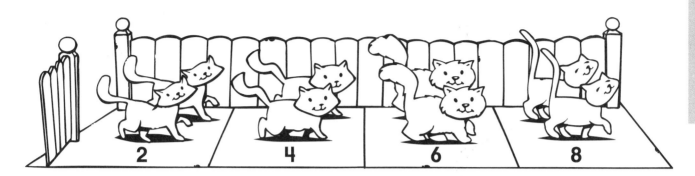

Eight big cats walk two by two.

Count by 2's. Write the numbers.

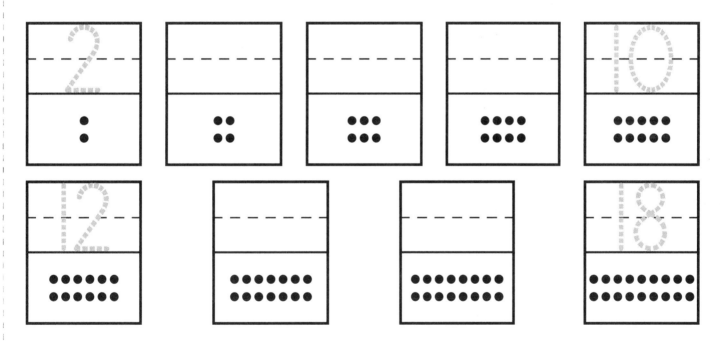

Write the answer.

What kind of 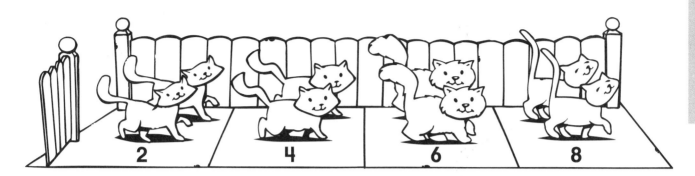s grow in 2's?

_____

_ _ _ _ _ _ _ _ _ _ _ _ _ _

_____ **trees**

Home for Twos

2 4 6 8 10 12 14 16 18 20 22 24 26 28 30

Count by 2's to connect the dots.
Color the picture.

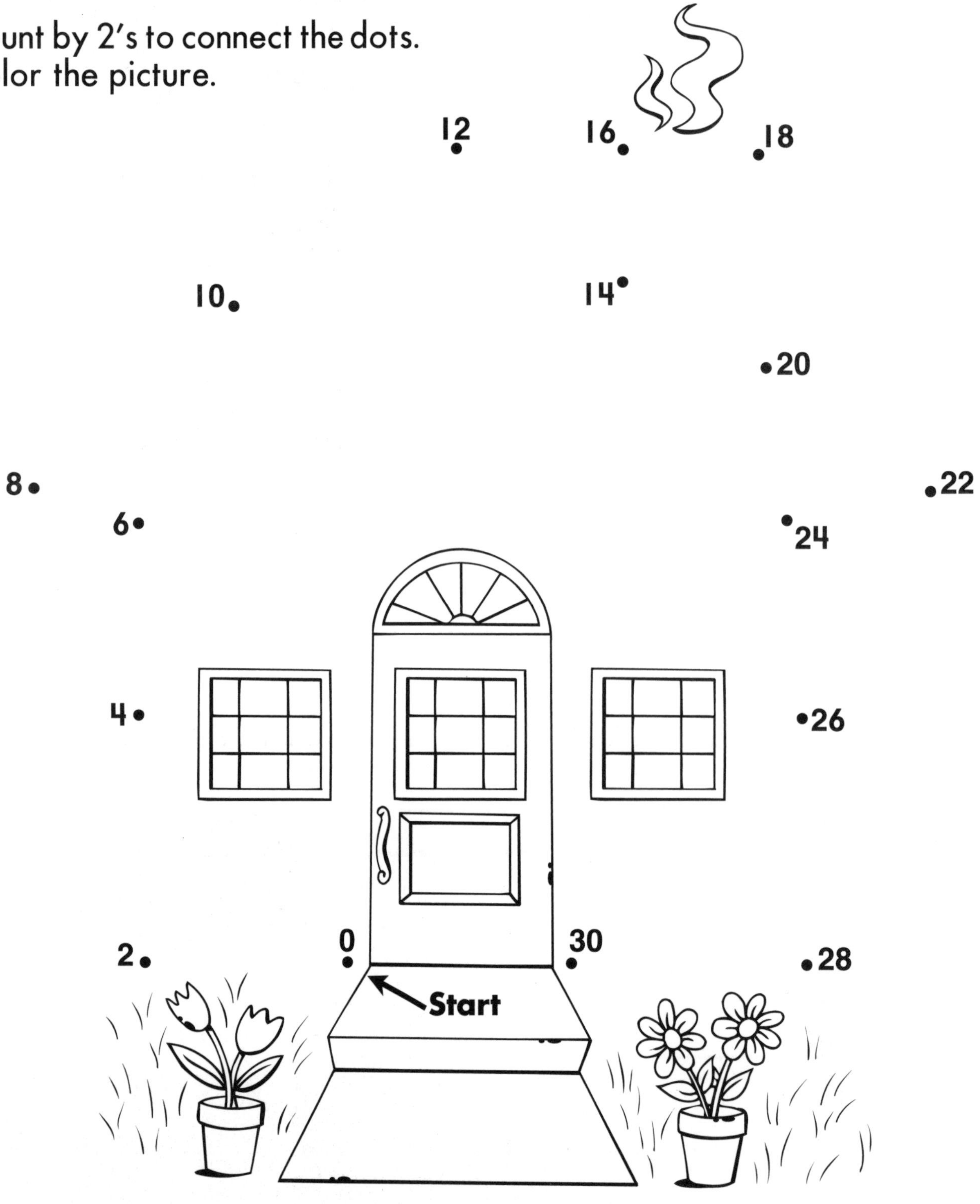

12

16

18

10

14

20

8

22

6

24

4

26

2

0

30

28

Start

Counting and sequencing numbers by 2's

How Many Shoes?

Count by 2's. Write the number.

_____

- - - - - - -

_____

_____

- - - - - - -

_____

_____

- - - - - - -

_____

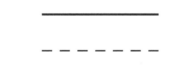 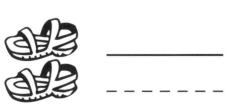

_____

- - - - - - -

_____

_____

- - - - - - -

_____

Counting by 5's

Count by 5's to 50. Say the numbers.

5 10 15 20 25 30 35 40 45 50
55 60 65 70 75 80 85 90 95 100

Count by 5's. Write the missing numbers.

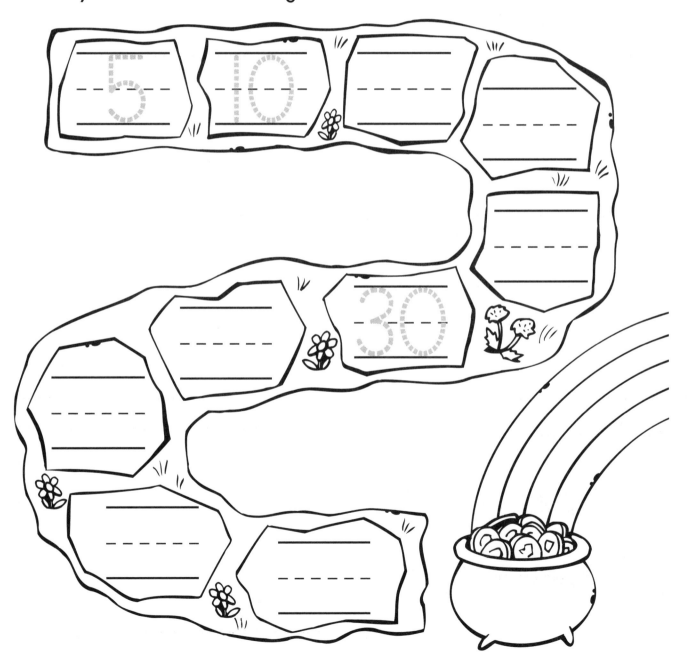

Counting and writing numbers by 5's

Give Me Five

1¢ 1¢	1¢ 1¢	1¢ 1¢	1¢ 1¢
1¢ 1¢	1¢ 1¢	1¢ 1¢	1¢ 1¢
1¢ **5**	1¢ **10**	1¢ **15**	1¢ **20**

Count by 5's to 50. Write the numbers.

5 ___ 10 ___ ___ ___ 25

30 ___ ___ ___ 50

Draw the answer.

1 pickle for a 5¢ **.**

How many 1¢ **s?**

A-maze-ing Fives

Count by 5's to draw a path through the maze.

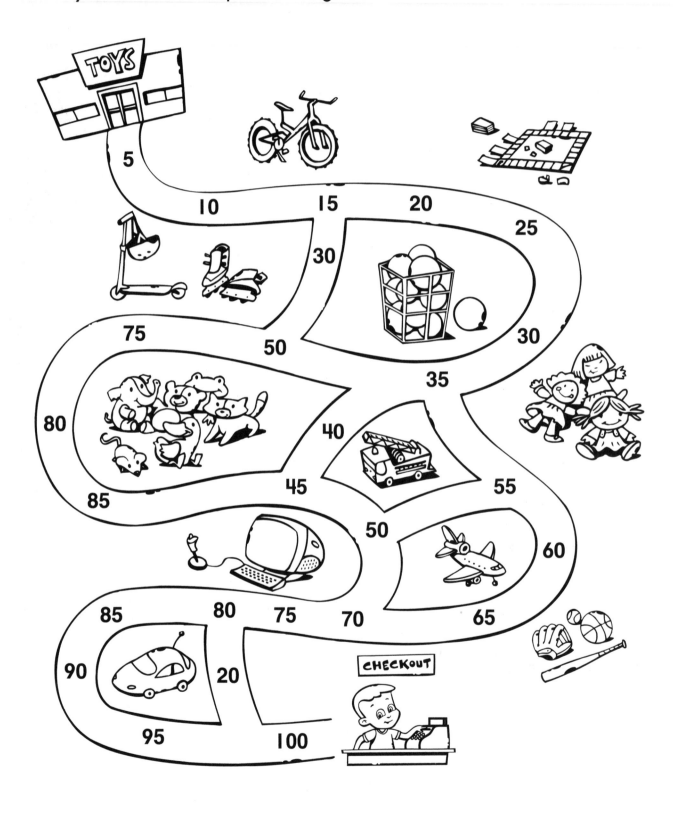

Counting and sequencing numbers by 5's

Counting by 10's

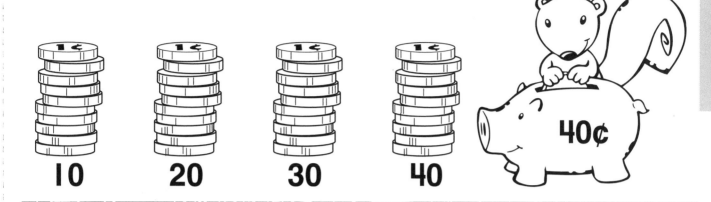

10 **20** **30** **40**

Count by 10's to 100. Write the numbers.

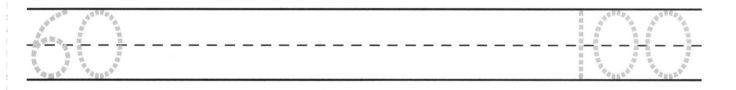

Count 10 s at a time,

or swap them for a .

How many s equal

these stacks of (1¢)s?

_____

_ _ _ _ _ _

Write the number._____

Counting and writing numbers by 10's   **17**

Counting Marbles

Count by 10's. Write the number.

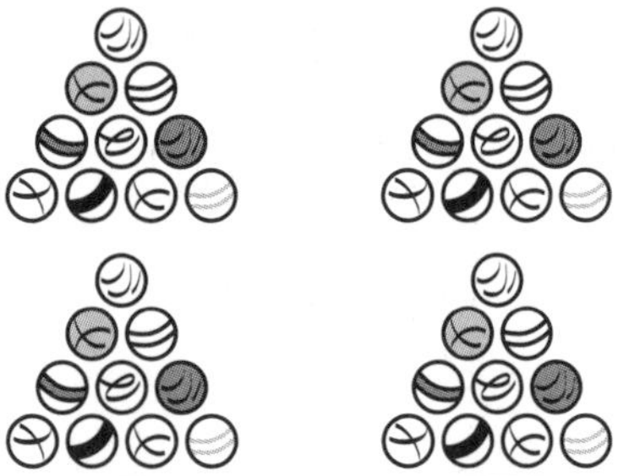

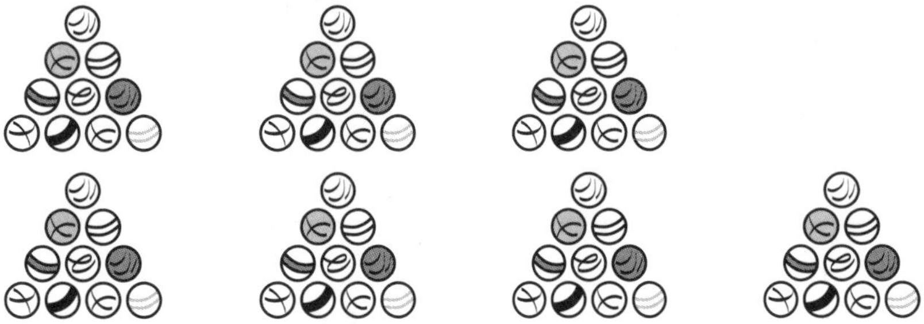

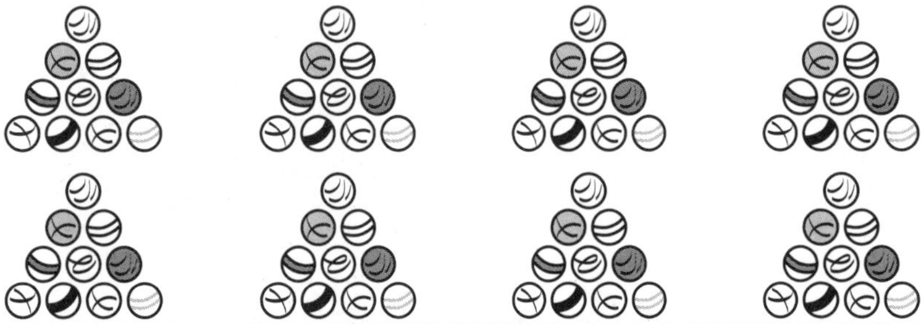

_____

_ _ _ _ _ _ _ _ _

_____

_____

_ _ _ _ _ _ _ _ _

_____

_____

_ _ _ _ _ _ _ _ _

_____

_____

_ _ _ _ _ _ _ _ _

_____

_____

_ _ _ _ _ _ _ _ _

_____

Counting and writing numbers by 10's

Missing Tens

Count by 10's. Write the missing numbers. Color the caterpillars.

| 10 | 20 | 30 | 40 | 50 | 60 | 70 | 80 | 90 | 100 |

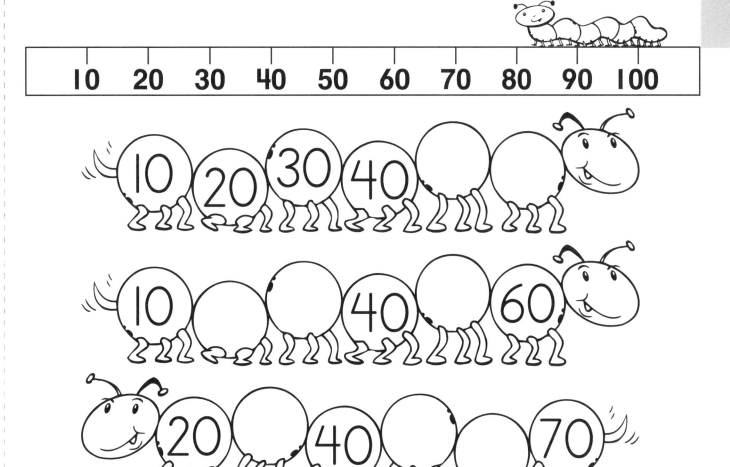

Chart Your Way

Write the numbers to finish the chart.

1	2			5			8		10
11		13				17		19	20
21			24	25				29	30
31		33			36		38	39	
	42		44			47			50
51				55	56				60
61			64			67		69	
71		73			76				80
	82			85			88		90
91			94		96		98		100

Count by 2's. Color the boxes yellow.
Count by 5's. Circle the numbers in red.
Count by 10's. Outline the boxes in blue.

Counting and writing numbers from 1–100

Zoo Detective

Look at the pictures in the chart. What numbers belong there?
Write the number beside each picture below.

1	2	3	4	5	6		8	9	10
11	12	13	14	15		17	18	19	20
21	22		24	25	26	27	28		30
31	32	33	34	35	36		38	39	40
	42	43	44	45	46	47	48	49	50
51	52	53		55	56	57	58	59	
61	62	63	64	65		67	68	69	70
71		73	74	75	76	77	78	79	80
81	82	83	84		86	87	88	89	90
91	92	93	94	95	96		98	99	100

Counting and writing numbers from 1–100

One More, One Less

  4 is **one more** than 3.
3 is **one less** than 4.

Draw **one more**. Write the number.

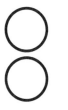

How many?

7

How many?

Show **one less**. Write the number.

How many?

How many?

Constructing and recording sets with one more or one less

Counting Bears

 5 is **more** than 2.

Circle the number that is **more**.

1	(4)	3	6
6	8	9	11
10	7	15	12

Identifying the set that shows more

23

So Many Hats

Color the set in each row that shows **less**.

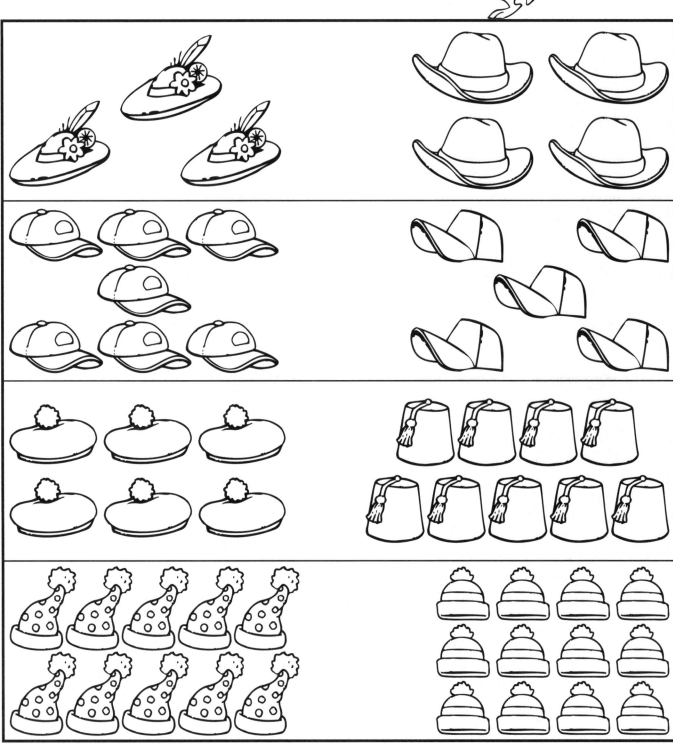

Identifying the set that shows less

Before

3 comes **before** 4.

Write the number that comes **before**.

After

5 comes **after** 4.

Write the number that comes **after**.

Writing the number that comes after

Between

4 comes **between** 3 and 5.

Write the number that comes **between**.

7 ____ 9	14 ____ 16
11 ____ 13	4 ____ 6
15 ____ 17	8 ____ 10
10 ____ 12	17 ____ 19

Larger and Smaller

5 is the **larger** number.
3 is the **smaller** number.

Color the box with the **larger** number.

9	4

13	15

7	9

6	8

10	11

19	16

Color the box with the **smaller** number.

5	6

13	11

8	10

12	20

18	15

17	12

Identifying larger and smaller numbers

Largest and Smallest

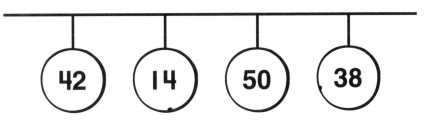

50 is the **largest** number.
14 is the **smallest** number.

Circle the **largest** number. Draw a square around the **smallest** number.

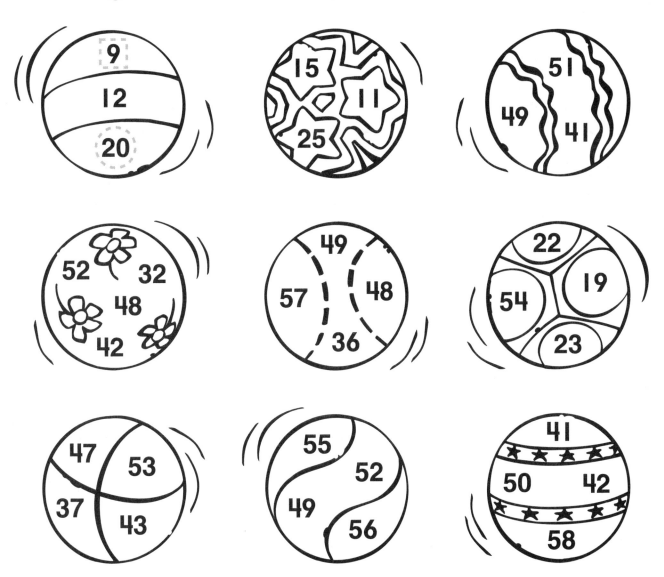

50 More or Less

If a box shows a number **less than** 50, color it yellow.
If a box shows a number **more than** 50, color it blue.

53	75	62	42	61	67	58
71	49	25	38	68	33	73
51	65	66	22	70	27	60
46	10	59	36	74	47	62
53	57	63	29	69	72	64

Look at the boxes you colored.
Write the number you see.

_____

_ _ _ _ _ _ _

_____

Comparing 2-digit numbers

Roller Coaster

Write the missing numbers.

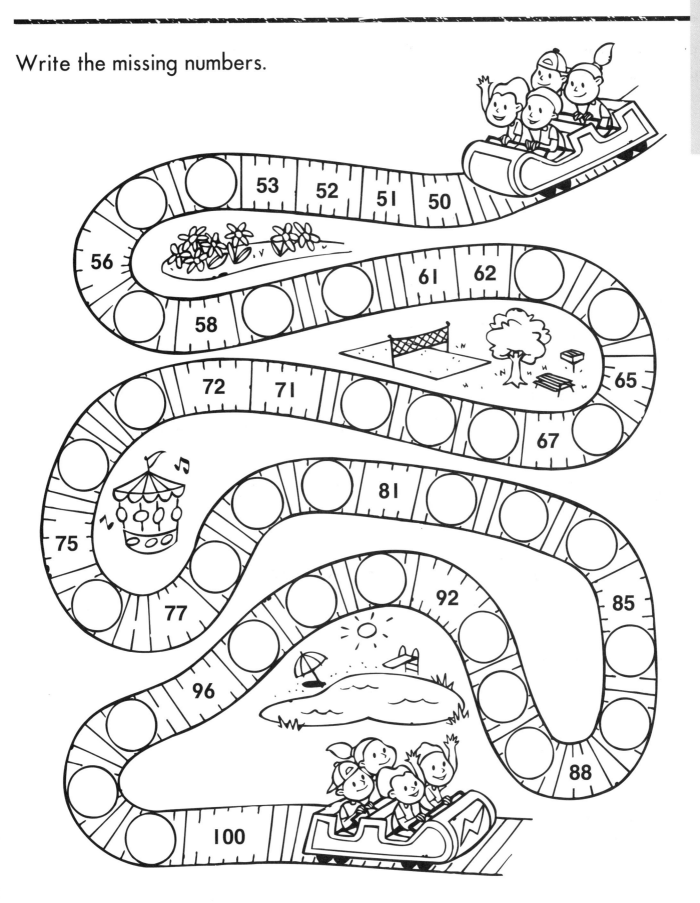

Garden Path

Color the boxes from 75 to 100, in order,
to make a path from Start to Finish.
Then color the rest of the picture.

Start

75	76	77	80	81	93	94
78	71	78	79	91	80	83
72	89	79	83	93	94	95
82	81	80	88	92	91	96
83	88	79	72	91	98	97
84	76	75	78	90	92	98
85	86	87	88	89	93	99
88	92	94	93	91	87	100

Finish

Sequencing numbers to 100

Answer Key

As the child completes the pages in this section, review his or her answers. When you take the time to correct the work and explain mistakes, you're showing your child that you feel learning is important.

page 2

page 3

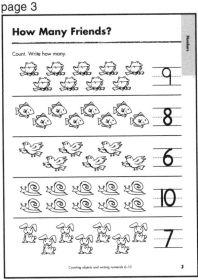

page 4

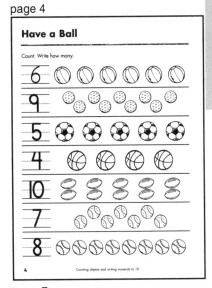

page 5

page 6

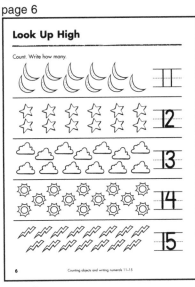

page 7

page 8

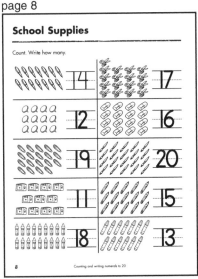

page 9

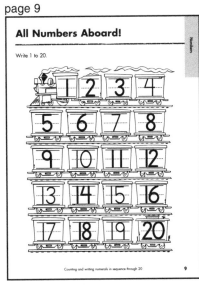

page 10

Counting by 2's

Home for Twos

2 4 6 8 10 12 14 16 18 20 22 24 26 28 30

Count by 2's to connect the dots.
Color the picture.

How Many Shoes?

Count by 2's. Write the number.

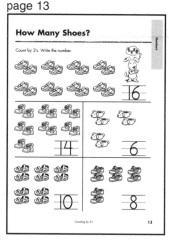

Counting by 5's

Count by 5's to 50. Say the numbers.
5 10 15 20 25 30 35 40 45 50
55 60 65 70 75 80 85 90 95 100

Count by 5's. Write the missing numbers.

Give Me Five

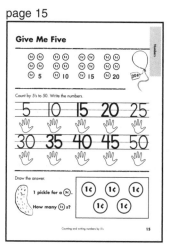

A-maze-ing Fives

Count by 5's to draw a path through the maze.

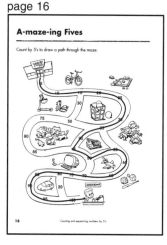

Counting by 10's

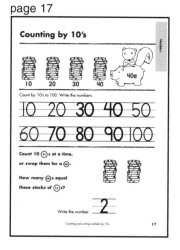

Counting Marbles

Count by 10's. Write the number.

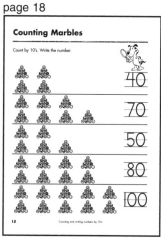

Missing Tens

Count by 10's. Write the missing numbers. Color the caterpillars.

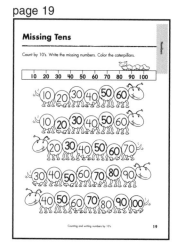

Chart Your Way

Write the numbers to finish the chart.

Zoo Detective

Look at the pictures in the chart. What numbers belong there?
Write the number beside each picture below.

One More, One Less

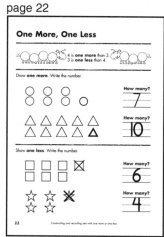

page 23

Counting Bears

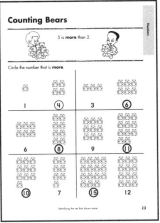

5 is **more** than 2.

Circle the number that is **more**.

1	④	3	⑥
6	⑧	9	⑪
⑩	7	⑮	12

Identifying the set that shows more 23

page 24

So Many Hats

Color the set in each row that shows **less**.

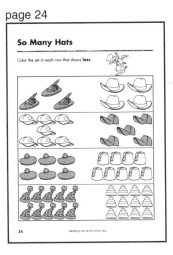

24 Identifying the set that shows less

page 25

Before

3 comes **before** 4.

Write the number that comes **before**.

6	7	10	11
13	14	7	8
4	5	17	18
9	10	14	15

Writing the number that comes before 25

page 26

After

5 comes **after** 4.

Write the number that comes **after**.

10	11	2	3
15	16	7	8
18	19	13	14

26 Writing the number that comes after

page 27

Between

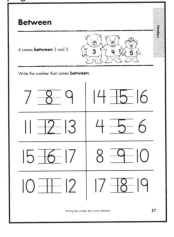

4 comes **between** 3 and 5.

Write the number that comes **between**.

7	8	9	14	15	16
11	12	13	4	5	6
15	16	17	8	9	10
10	11	12	17	18	19

Writing the number that comes between 27

page 28

Larger and Smaller

5 is the **larger** number.
3 is the **smaller** number.

Color the box with the **larger** number.

9	4	13	15	7	9
6	8	10	11	19	16

Color the box with the **smaller** number.

5	6	13	11	8	10
12	20	18	15	17	12

28 Identifying larger and smaller numbers

page 29

Largest and Smallest

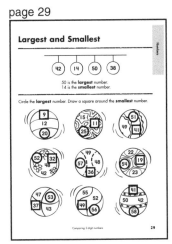

42 14 50 38

50 is the **largest** number.
14 is the **smallest** number.

Circle the **largest** number. Draw a square around the **smallest** number.

Comparing 2-digit numbers 29

page 30

50 More or Less

If a box shows a number **less than** 50, color it yellow.
If a box shows a number **more than** 50, color it blue.

53	75	62	42	61	67	58
71	49	25	38	68	33	73
51	65	66	22	70	27	60
46	10	59	36	74	47	62
53	57	63	29	69	72	64

Look at the boxes you colored.
Write the number you see.   50

30 Comparing 2-digit numbers

page 31

Roller Coaster

Write the missing numbers.

Sequencing and writing numbers to 100 31

page 32

Garden Path

Color the boxes from 75 to 100, in order,
to make a path from Start to Finish. Then
color the rest of the picture.

Start

75	76	77	80	81	93	94
78	71	78	79	91	80	83
72	89	79	83	93	94	95
82	81	80	88	92	91	96
83	88	79	72	91	98	97
84	76	75	78	90	92	98
85	86	87	88	89	93	99
88	92	94	93	91	87	100

Finish

32 Sequencing numbers to 100

So Many Flowers

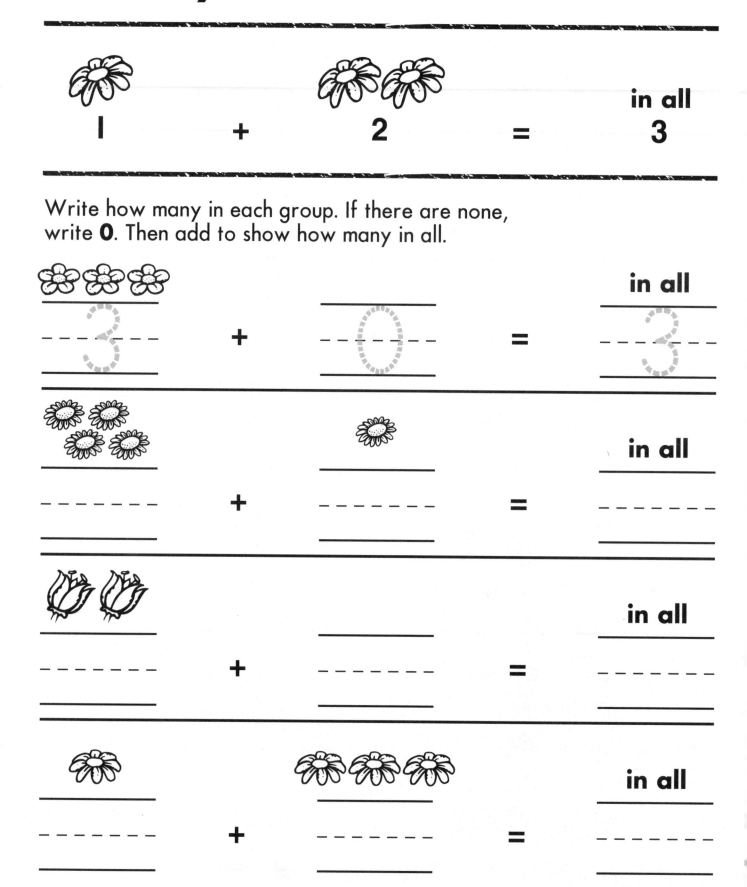

1 + 2 = **in all** 3

Write how many in each group. If there are none,
write **0**. Then add to show how many in all.

3 + 0 = **in all** 3

___ + ___ = **in all** ___

___ + ___ = **in all** ___

___ + ___ = **in all** ___

Adding numbers to 5; using 0 (zero)

Collecting Sums

Add. Write the sum.

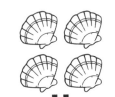 0 + 4 = _____

 2 + 3 = _____

2 + 2 = _____

3
+ 1
_____
_____

2
+ 1
_____
_____

3
+ 2
_____
_____

1
+ 3
_____
_____

2
+ 0
_____
_____

0
+ 5
_____
_____

Animal Math

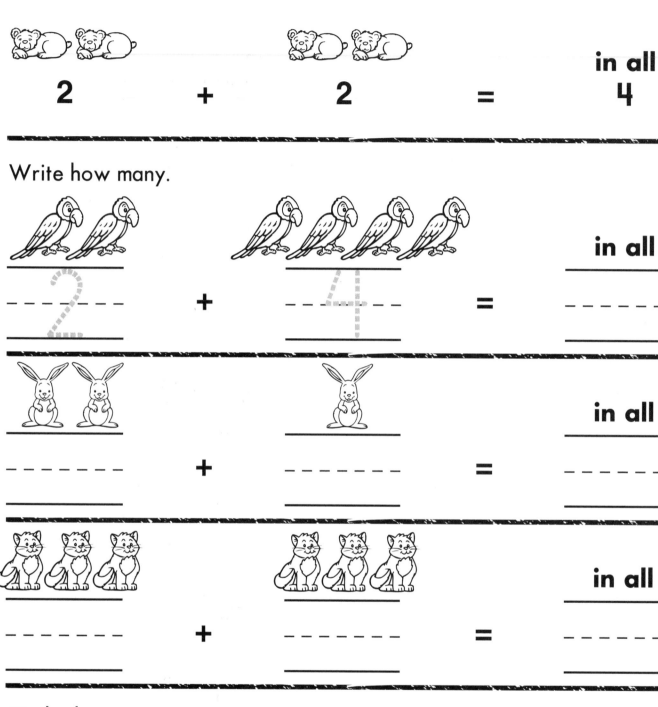

2 + 2 = **in all** 4

Write how many.

2 + 4 = **in all**

___ + ___ = **in all**

___ + ___ = **in all**

Circle the answer.

There are 6 s in all.

How many are hiding?

2

4

Adding numbers to 6

Adding Treats

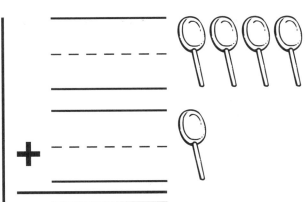

$$\begin{array}{r} 3 \\ +\ 2 \\ \hline 5 \end{array} \text{ in all}$$

Write how many.

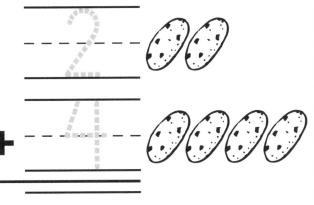

$$\begin{array}{r} \underline{\hspace{2cm}} \\ +\ \underline{\hspace{2cm}} \\ \hline \underline{\hspace{2cm}} \text{ in all} \end{array}$$

$$\begin{array}{r} \underline{\hspace{2cm}} \\ +\ \underline{\hspace{2cm}} \\ \hline \underline{\hspace{2cm}} \text{ in all} \end{array}$$

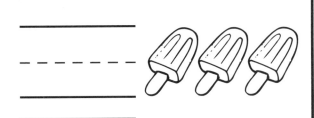

$$\begin{array}{r} \underline{\hspace{2cm}} \\ +\ \underline{\hspace{2cm}} \\ \hline \underline{\hspace{2cm}} \text{ in all} \end{array}$$

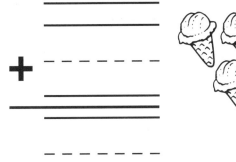

$$\begin{array}{r} \underline{\hspace{2cm}} \\ +\ \underline{\hspace{2cm}} \\ \hline \underline{\hspace{2cm}} \text{ in all} \end{array}$$

Circle the answer.

There are 6 s in all.

How many are in the bag?

1   2

Grocery Store

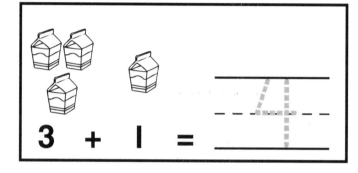

$$4 \quad + \quad 2 \quad = \quad 6$$

Add. Write the sum.

$3 + 1 = \underline{}$

$3 + 3 = \underline{}$

$5 + 1 = \underline{}$

$1 + 2 = \underline{}$

$2 + 2 = \underline{}$

$2 + 4 = \underline{}$

$0 + 5 = \underline{}$

$2 + 3 = \underline{}$

$4 + 1 = \underline{}$

$0 + 6 = \underline{}$

Finding sums to 6

Frosty Fun

    **in all**

5   +   3   =   8

Write how many.

      **in all**

_____   _____

- - 4 - -   +   - - 4 - -   =   - - - - -

_____   _____

      **in all**

_____   _____

- - - - - -   +   - - - - -   =   - - - - -

_____   _____

   **in all**

_____   _____

- - - - - -   +   - - - - -   =   - - - - -

_____   _____

   **in all**

_____   _____

- - - - - -   +   - - - - -   =   - - - - -

_____   _____

Cooking Up Breakfast Fun

How many s?

Color to show the numbers.

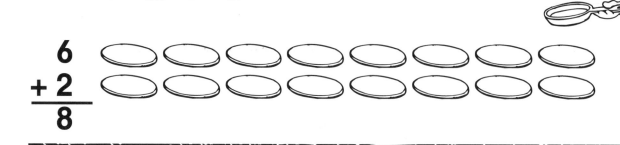

$\begin{array}{r} 6 \\ + 2 \\ \hline 8 \end{array}$

Add. Write the sum.

$\begin{array}{r} 3 \\ + 2 \\ \hline \end{array}$

$\begin{array}{r} 5 \\ + 3 \\ \hline \end{array}$

$\begin{array}{r} 4 \\ + 2 \\ \hline \end{array}$

$\begin{array}{r} 3 \\ + 3 \\ \hline \end{array}$

$\begin{array}{r} 8 \\ + 0 \\ \hline \end{array}$

$\begin{array}{r} 0 \\ + 6 \\ \hline \end{array}$

$\begin{array}{r} 7 \\ + 1 \\ \hline \end{array}$

$\begin{array}{r} 4 \\ + 3 \\ \hline \end{array}$

Finding sums to 8

Tennis, Anyone?

7   **+**   **3**   **=**   **in all**
                                                           10

Write how many.

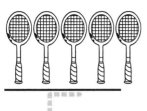      **in all**

_ _ _ _ _ _   **+**   _ _ _ _ _ _   **=**   _ _ _ _ _ _

   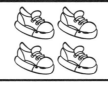   **in all**

_ _ _ _ _ _   **+**   _ _ _ _ _ _   **=**   _ _ _ _ _ _

 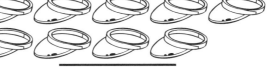   **in all**

_ _ _ _ _ _   **+**   _ _ _ _ _ _   **=**   _ _ _ _ _ _

      **in all**

_ _ _ _ _ _   **+**   _ _ _ _ _ _   **=**   _ _ _ _ _ _

Math Hats

Add to find the sums. Color the hats with sums of 10.

$$7 + 3$$

$$5 + 4$$

$$4 + 3$$

$$0 + 9$$

$$5 + 5$$

$$3 + 6$$

$$2 + 8$$

$$3 + 5$$

$$6 + 4$$

Finding sums to 10

Oh, How Colorful!

Color the sections for the sums using the code.
Then finish coloring the picture.

| 10 = red | 9 = blue | 8 = green |
| 7 = yellow | 6 = orange | |

Turn-Arounds

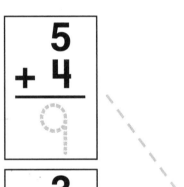

4
+ 3
———
7

The sum is the same.

3
+ 4
———
7

Write the sums. Then match.

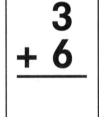

5 + 4 —— 9	2 + 6 ——
3 + 7 ——	4 + 5 —— 9
6 + 2 ——	7 + 0 ——
0 + 7 ——	7 + 3 ——

3 + 6 ——	4 + 6 ——
5 + 5 ——	6 + 3 ——
6 + 4 ——	5 + 5 ——

Using turnaround addition facts to find sums

Seashells

3
+9
---
12 **in all**

Write how many.

_____

- - - - - - -

_____

+ _____

- - - - - - -

_____ **in all**

_____

- - - - - - -

_____

+ _____

- - - - - - -

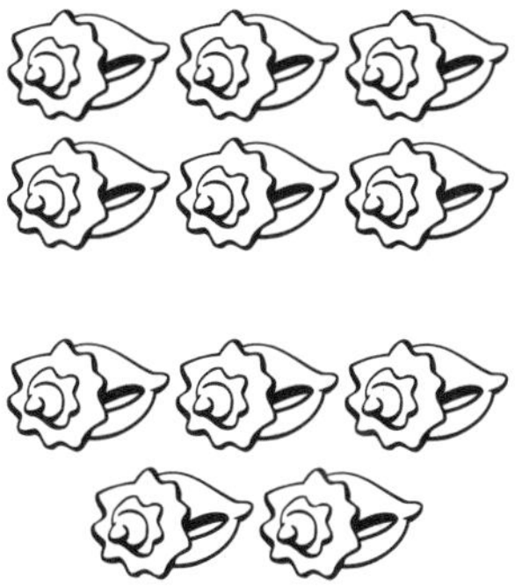

_____ **in all**

_____

- - - - - - -

_____

+ _____

- - - - - - -

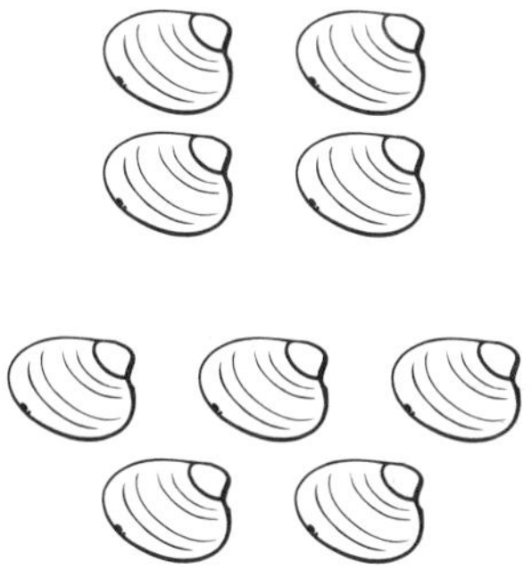

_____ **in all**

_____

- - - - - - -

_____

+ _____

- - - - - - -

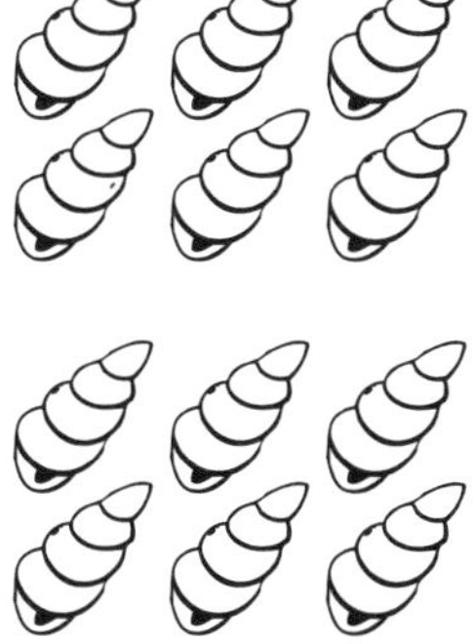

_____ **in all**

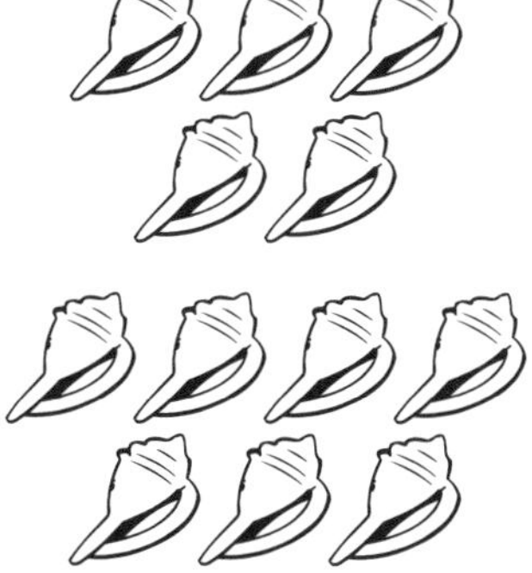

Domino Dots

$9 + 3 = \underline{12}$

$\begin{array}{r} 3 \\ + 9 \\ \hline 12 \end{array}$

Add. Color the dominos with sums of 10 or more.

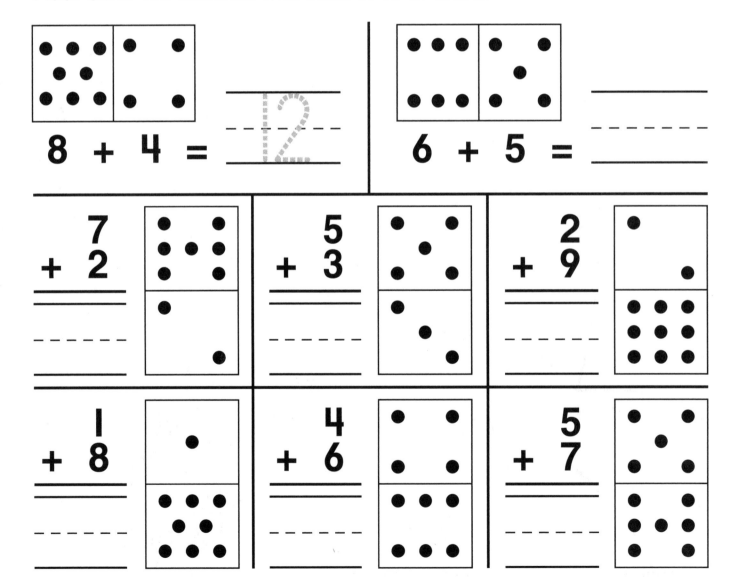

$8 + 4 = \underline{12}$

$6 + 5 = \underline{\quad}$

$\begin{array}{r} 7 \\ + 2 \\ \hline \end{array}$

$\begin{array}{r} 5 \\ + 3 \\ \hline \end{array}$

$\begin{array}{r} 2 \\ + 9 \\ \hline \end{array}$

$\begin{array}{r} 1 \\ + 8 \\ \hline \end{array}$

$\begin{array}{r} 4 \\ + 6 \\ \hline \end{array}$

$\begin{array}{r} 5 \\ + 7 \\ \hline \end{array}$

Finding sums to 12

Rainy Day Math

Add. Then color the sections for the sums using the code.

9 = yellow	11 = blue
10 = green	12 = red

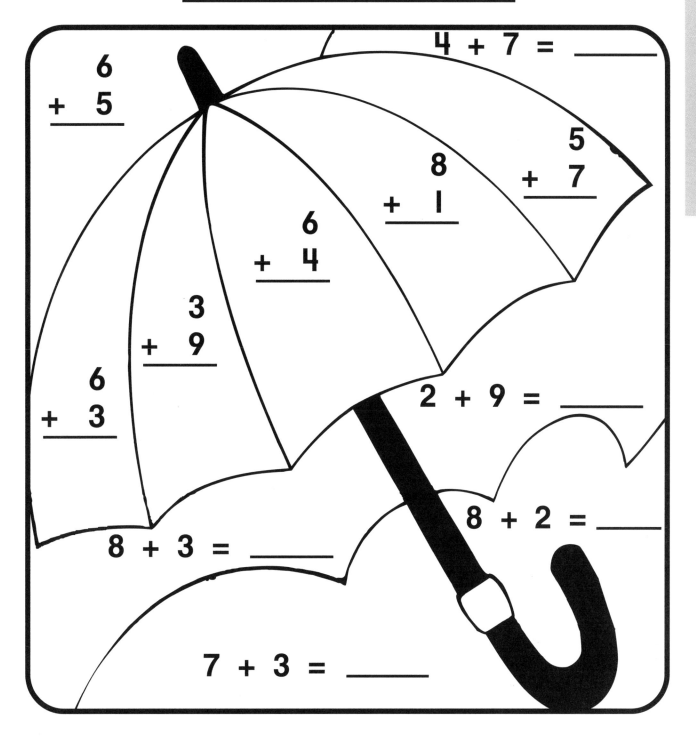

Flower Show

9
+ 6
15 in all

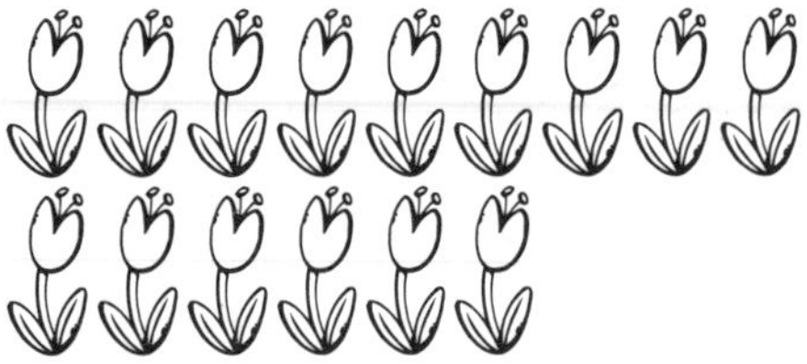

7
+ 7
14 in all

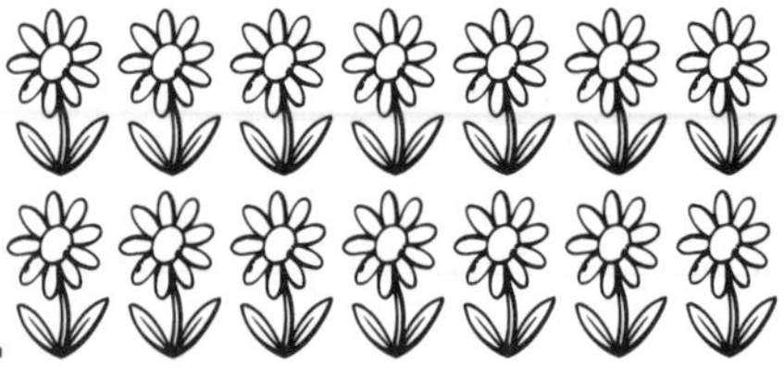

Write how many.

5
+ 7
____ in all

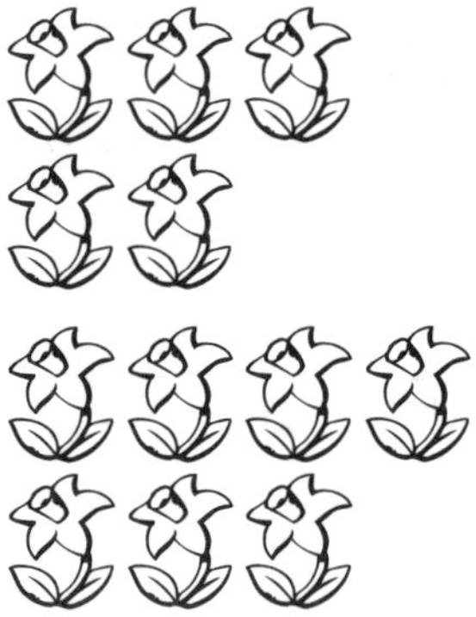

____
+ ____
____ in all

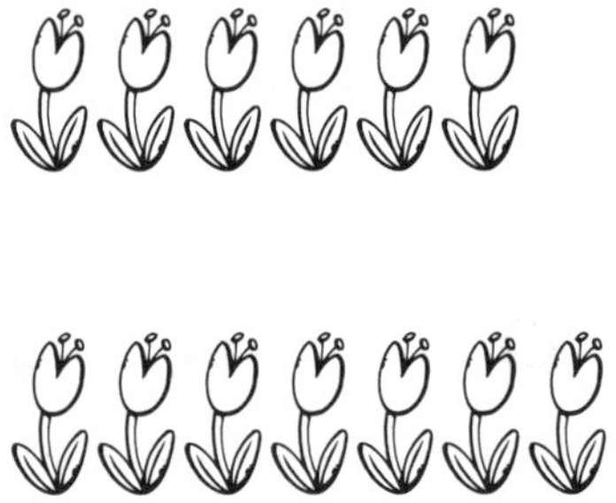

____
+ ____
____ in all

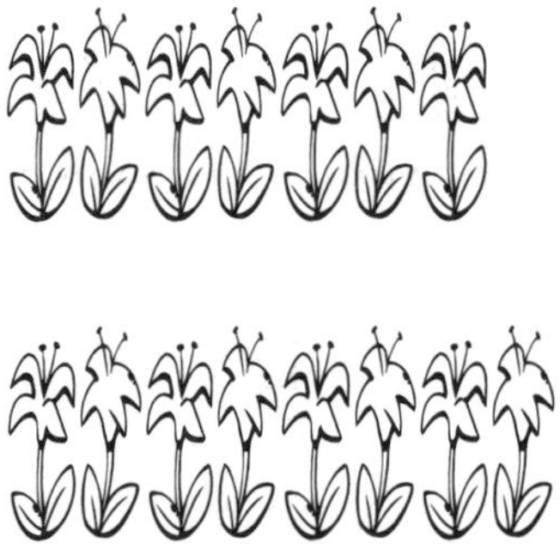

____
+ ____
____ in all

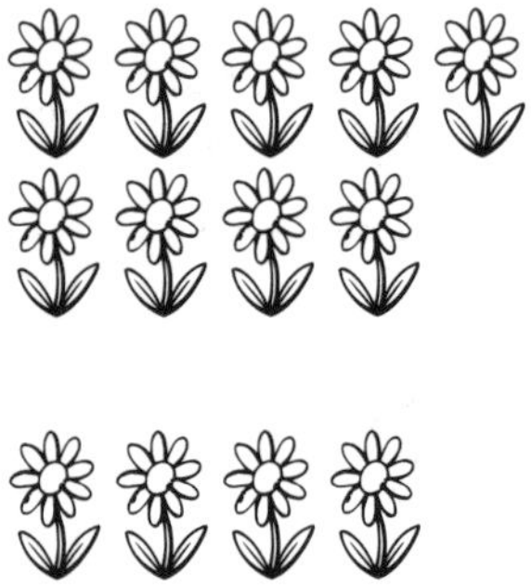

Cars and Blocks

 8 + 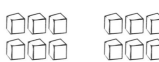 7 = 15

Add.

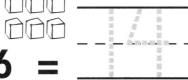

8 + 6 = _14_

6 + 7 = _____

9 + 5 = _____

8 + 7 = _____

6 + 8 = _____

7 + 4 = _____

7 + 7 = _____

6 + 9 = _____

What's next?

$\begin{array}{r} 9 \\ + 3 \\ \hline \end{array}$

$\begin{array}{r} 9 \\ + 4 \\ \hline \end{array}$

$\begin{array}{r} 9 \\ + 5 \\ \hline \end{array}$

$\begin{array}{r} 9 \\ + \boxed{} \\ \hline \end{array}$

Review

Add.

$$\begin{array}{r} 5 \\ + 6 \\ \hline \end{array} \qquad \begin{array}{r} 3 \\ + 9 \\ \hline \end{array} \qquad \begin{array}{r} 6 \\ + 7 \\ \hline \end{array} \qquad \begin{array}{r} 9 \\ + 4 \\ \hline \end{array}$$

$$\begin{array}{r} 8 \\ + 6 \\ \hline \end{array} \qquad \begin{array}{r} 2 \\ + 9 \\ \hline \end{array} \qquad \begin{array}{r} 9 \\ + 0 \\ \hline \end{array} \qquad \begin{array}{r} 8 \\ + 3 \\ \hline \end{array} \qquad \begin{array}{r} 7 \\ + 4 \\ \hline \end{array}$$

$$\begin{array}{r} 9 \\ + 5 \\ \hline \end{array} \qquad \begin{array}{r} 7 \\ + 7 \\ \hline \end{array} \qquad \begin{array}{r} 4 \\ + 4 \\ \hline \end{array} \qquad \begin{array}{r} 9 \\ + 6 \\ \hline \end{array} \qquad \begin{array}{r} 7 \\ + 3 \\ \hline \end{array}$$

$$\begin{array}{r} 4 \\ + 8 \\ \hline \end{array} \qquad \begin{array}{r} 6 \\ + 2 \\ \hline \end{array} \qquad \begin{array}{r} 6 \\ + 6 \\ \hline \end{array} \qquad \begin{array}{r} 8 \\ + 5 \\ \hline \end{array} \qquad \begin{array}{r} 7 \\ + 8 \\ \hline \end{array}$$

Kitten Mischief

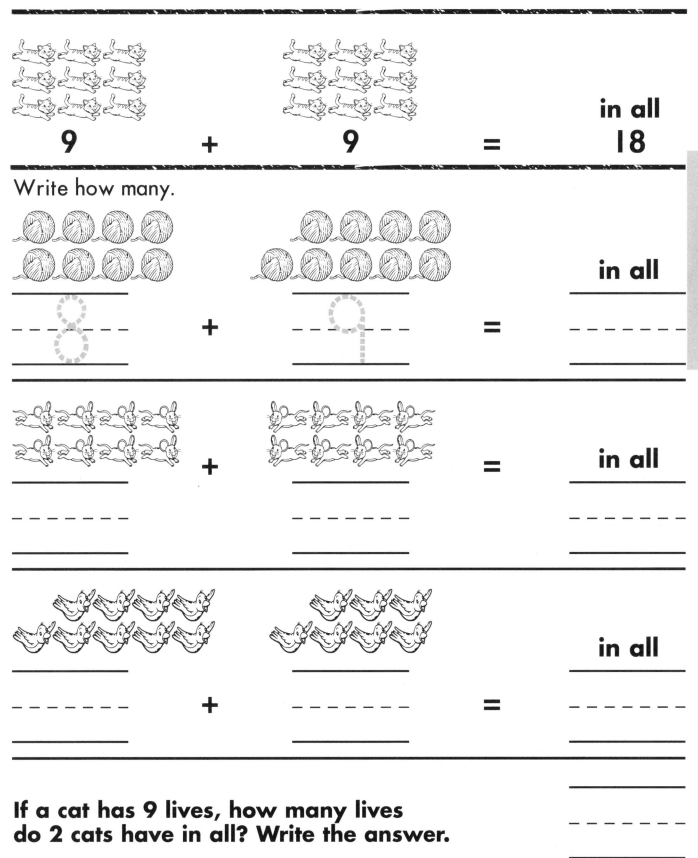

9 + 9 = in all 18

Write how many.

___ 8 ___ + ___ 9 ___ = ___ in all ___

___ + ___ = ___ in all ___

___ + ___ = ___ in all ___

If a cat has 9 lives, how many lives do 2 cats have in all? Write the answer.

___

Marching Band

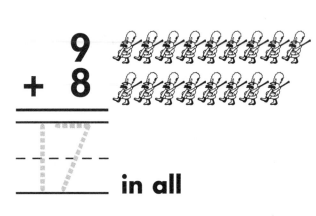

$$\begin{array}{r} 9 \\ + 8 \\ \hline \end{array}$$

____ in all

Write how many in all.

$$\begin{array}{r} 8 \\ + 7 \\ \hline \end{array}$$

____ in all

$$\begin{array}{r} 8 \\ + 9 \\ \hline \end{array}$$

____ in all

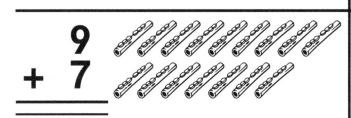

$$\begin{array}{r} 9 \\ + 7 \\ \hline \end{array}$$

____ in all

$$\begin{array}{r} 6 \\ + 9 \\ \hline \end{array}$$

____ in all

$$\begin{array}{r} 6 \\ + 7 \\ \hline \end{array}$$

____ in all

$$\begin{array}{r} 7 \\ + 7 \\ \hline \end{array}$$

____ in all

Adding numbers to 18

On the Green

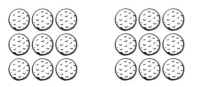

$$9 + 9 = 18$$

Add.

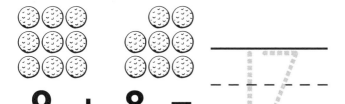

$$9 + 8 = \underline{7}$$

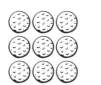

$$9 + 7 = \underline{\qquad}$$

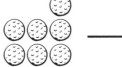

$8+9 = \underline{\qquad}$ $7+9 = \underline{\qquad}$ $9+6 = \underline{\qquad}$

$8+8 = \underline{\qquad}$ $7+3 = \underline{\qquad}$ $0+7 = \underline{\qquad}$

$2+6 = \underline{\qquad}$ $8+0 = \underline{\qquad}$ $6+3 = \underline{\qquad}$

Fish for Tens and Ones

Circle the groups of ten. Write how many tens and ones.
Then write how many in all.

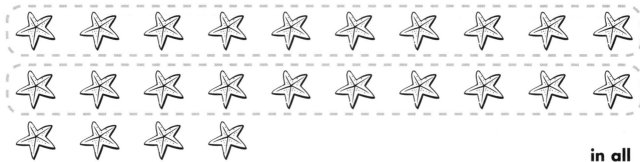

in all
2 tens + 4 ones = 24

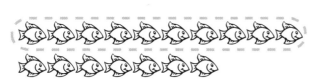

in all

___ **tens** + ___ **ones** = ___

in all

___ **tens** + ___ **ones** = ___

in all

___ **tens** + ___ **ones** = ___

in all

___ **tens** + ___ **ones** = ___

in all

___ **tens** + ___ **ones** = ___

in all

___ **tens** + ___ **ones** = ___

Counting groups of tens and ones; adding

Good and Fruity

Write how many tens and ones. Then write how many in all.

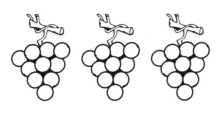 

in all

_____ + _____ = _____
  tens   ones

in all

_____ + _____ = _____
  tens   ones

in all

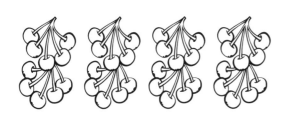

_____ + _____ = _____
  tens   ones

Write how many tens and ones.

35 = ____ **tens** + ____ **ones** | **54** = ____ **tens** + ____ **ones**

81 = ____ **tens** + ____ **ones** | **29** = ____ **tens** + ____ **ones**

Write the number.

4 tens + 3 ones = _____   **1 ten + 6 ones =** _____

6 tens + 0 ones = _____   **9 tens + 9 ones =** _____

Lots of Squares

$$\begin{array}{r} 23 \\ +\ \ 4 \\ \hline 27 \end{array}\ \text{in all}$$

Count. Write how many in all.

$$\begin{array}{r} 13 \\ +\ \ 6 \\ \hline \end{array}$$

_____ in all

$$\begin{array}{r} 24 \\ +\ \ 2 \\ \hline \end{array}$$

_____ in all

$$\begin{array}{r} 52 \\ +\ \ 5 \\ \hline \end{array}$$

_____ in all

$$\begin{array}{r} 40 \\ +\ \ 7 \\ \hline \end{array}$$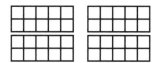

_____ in all

$$\begin{array}{r} 31 \\ +\ \ 4 \\ \hline \end{array}$$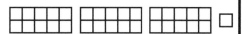

_____ in all

$$\begin{array}{r} 63 \\ +\ \ 3 \\ \hline \end{array}$$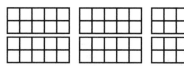

_____ in all

Counting to add tens and ones

Fun in Tenstown

In Tenstown, everything comes in packs of 10.

tens	ones
3	0
+2	0
5	0

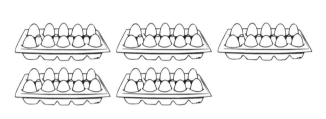 

First add the ones. Then add the tens.

tens	ones		tens	ones
4	0		7	0
+1	0		+2	0
5	0			

$$\begin{array}{r} 30 \\ +30 \\ \hline \end{array} \quad \begin{array}{r} 10 \\ +70 \\ \hline \end{array} \quad \begin{array}{r} 40 \\ +30 \\ \hline \end{array} \quad \begin{array}{r} 50 \\ +20 \\ \hline \end{array} \quad \begin{array}{r} 60 \\ +30 \\ \hline \end{array} \quad \begin{array}{r} 50 \\ +40 \\ \hline \end{array}$$

$$\begin{array}{r} 60 \\ +20 \\ \hline \end{array} \quad \begin{array}{r} 50 \\ +30 \\ \hline \end{array} \quad \begin{array}{r} 80 \\ +10 \\ \hline \end{array} \quad \begin{array}{r} 40 \\ +20 \\ \hline \end{array} \quad \begin{array}{r} 10 \\ +40 \\ \hline \end{array} \quad \begin{array}{r} 40 \\ +40 \\ \hline \end{array}$$

More Fun in Tenstown

Sometimes there are extra ones in Tenstown.

20 trees

+ 3 trees

23 trees

First add the ones. Then add the tens.

tens	ones
3	4
+5	3
8	7

tens	ones
2	7
+3	0
5	7

$$\begin{array}{r} 51 \\ +38 \\ \hline \end{array}$$

$$\begin{array}{r} 62 \\ +25 \\ \hline \end{array}$$

$$\begin{array}{r} 31 \\ + 7 \\ \hline \end{array}$$

$$\begin{array}{r} 17 \\ +32 \\ \hline \end{array}$$

$$\begin{array}{r} 43 \\ + 6 \\ \hline \end{array}$$

$$\begin{array}{r} 71 \\ +26 \\ \hline \end{array}$$

$$\begin{array}{r} 44 \\ +44 \\ \hline \end{array}$$

Adding 1- and 2-digit numbers without regrouping

Pop the Balloons

First add the ones. Then add the tens. Write the sum.
Find the balloon with the same number and color it.

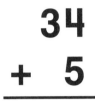

34 + 5	21 + 3	51 + 4	81 + 2
60 + 9	43 + 5	70 + 7	40 +30
60 +20	33 +23	42 +50	21 +72
53 +26	62 +16	43 +44	91 + 7

79
92
48
39
55
98
93
24
56
80
87
83
70
69
77
78

Addition

Adding 1- and 2-digit numbers without regrouping

Falling Leaves

First add the ones. Then add the tens. Color the picture.

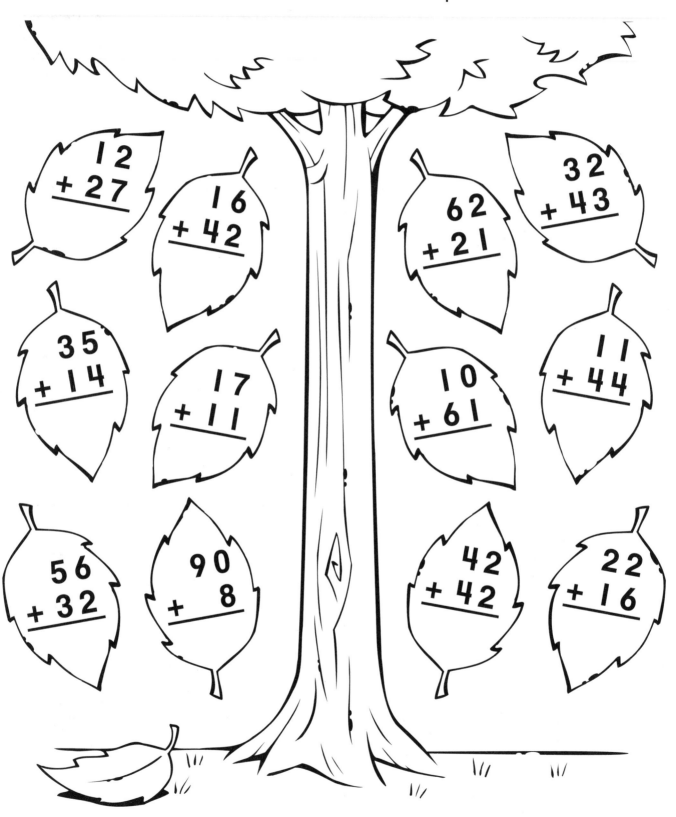

$$\begin{array}{r} 12 \\ + 27 \\ \hline \end{array}$$

$$\begin{array}{r} 16 \\ + 42 \\ \hline \end{array}$$

$$\begin{array}{r} 62 \\ + 21 \\ \hline \end{array}$$

$$\begin{array}{r} 32 \\ + 43 \\ \hline \end{array}$$

$$\begin{array}{r} 35 \\ + 14 \\ \hline \end{array}$$

$$\begin{array}{r} 17 \\ + 11 \\ \hline \end{array}$$

$$\begin{array}{r} 10 \\ + 61 \\ \hline \end{array}$$

$$\begin{array}{r} 11 \\ + 44 \\ \hline \end{array}$$

$$\begin{array}{r} 56 \\ + 32 \\ \hline \end{array}$$

$$\begin{array}{r} 90 \\ + 8 \\ \hline \end{array}$$

$$\begin{array}{r} 42 \\ + 42 \\ \hline \end{array}$$

$$\begin{array}{r} 22 \\ + 16 \\ \hline \end{array}$$

Adding 2-digit numbers without regrouping

Practice Test

First add the ones. Then add the tens.

$$\begin{array}{r} 11 \\ +\ 3 \\ \hline 14 \end{array}$$

○ 12
◉ 13
○ 14

A.
$$\begin{array}{r} 23 \\ +\ 1 \\ \hline \end{array}$$

○ 23
○ 24
○ 25

E.
$$\begin{array}{r} 40 \\ +30 \\ \hline \end{array}$$

○ 7
○ 70
○ 77

B.
$$\begin{array}{r} 65 \\ +\ 2 \\ \hline \end{array}$$

○ 60
○ 66
○ 67

F.
$$\begin{array}{r} 23 \\ +41 \\ \hline \end{array}$$

○ 22
○ 46
○ 64

C.
$$\begin{array}{r} 34 \\ +24 \\ \hline \end{array}$$

○ 38
○ 58
○ 54

G.
$$\begin{array}{r} 82 \\ +16 \\ \hline \end{array}$$

○ 98
○ 99
○ 88

D.
$$\begin{array}{r} 60 \\ +10 \\ \hline \end{array}$$

○ 7
○ 60
○ 70

H.
$$\begin{array}{r} 55 \\ +21 \\ \hline \end{array}$$

○ 65
○ 76
○ 56

Adding 1- and 2-digit numbers without regrouping

Answer Key

As the child completes the pages in this section, review his or her answers. When you take the time to correct the work and explain mistakes, you're showing your child that you feel learning is important.

page 36

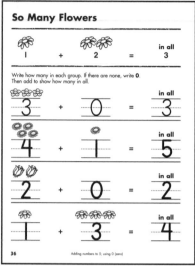

page 37

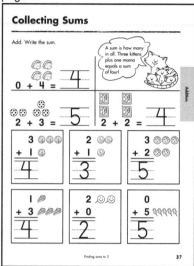

page 38

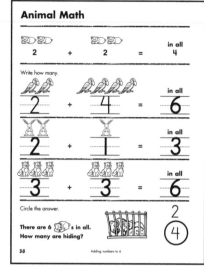

page 39

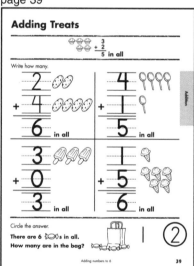

page 40

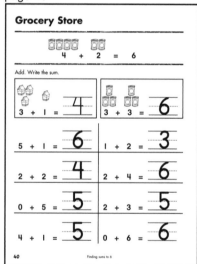

page 41

page 42

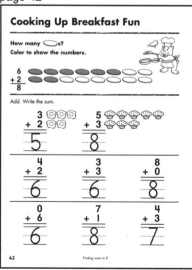

page 43

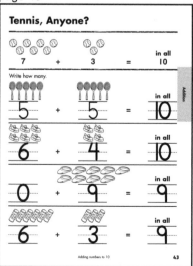

page 44

page 45

Oh, How Colorful!

Color the sections for the sums using the code. Then finish coloring the picture.

10 = red	9 = blue	8 = green
7 = yellow	6 = orange	

Reviewing sums to 10   45

page 46

Turn-Arounds

Using turnaround addition facts to find sums   46

page 47

Seashells

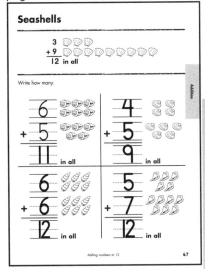

Adding numbers to 12   47

page 48

Domino Dots

Finding sums to 12   48

page 49

Rainy Day Math

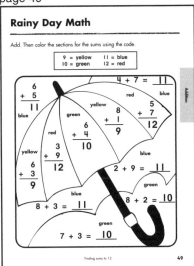

Finding sums to 12   49

page 50

Flower Show

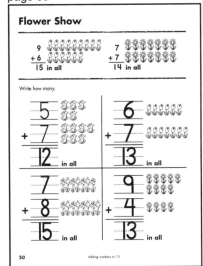

Adding numbers to 15   50

page 51

Cars and Blocks

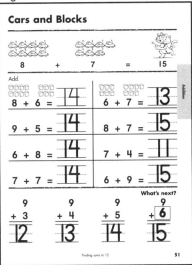

Finding sums to 15   51

page 52

Review

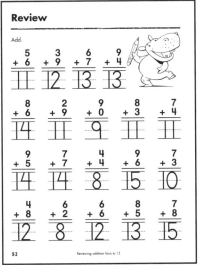

Reviewing addition facts to 15   52

page 53

Kitten Mischief

Adding numbers to 18   53

Addition

Answers

65

page 54

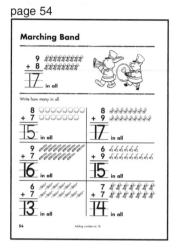

Marching Band

$$\begin{array}{r} 9 \\ + 8 \\ \hline 17 \end{array} \text{ in all}$$

Write how many in all.

$$\begin{array}{r} 8 \\ + 7 \\ \hline 15 \end{array} \text{ in all} \qquad \begin{array}{r} 8 \\ + 9 \\ \hline 17 \end{array} \text{ in all}$$

$$\begin{array}{r} 9 \\ + 7 \\ \hline 16 \end{array} \text{ in all} \qquad \begin{array}{r} 6 \\ + 9 \\ \hline 15 \end{array} \text{ in all}$$

$$\begin{array}{r} 6 \\ + 7 \\ \hline 13 \end{array} \text{ in all} \qquad \begin{array}{r} 7 \\ + 7 \\ \hline 14 \end{array} \text{ in all}$$

54   Adding numbers to 18

page 55

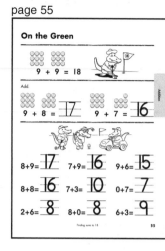

On the Green

$$9 + 9 = 18$$

Add.

$$9 + 8 = 17 \qquad 9 + 7 = 16$$

$$8+9= 17 \qquad 7+9= 16 \qquad 9+6= 15$$

$$8+8= 16 \qquad 7+3= 10 \qquad 0+7= 7$$

$$2+6= 8 \qquad 8+0= 8 \qquad 6+3= 9$$

Finding sums to 18   55

page 56

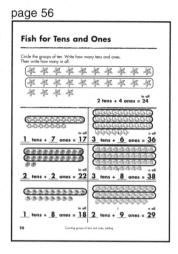

Fish for Tens and Ones

Circle the groups of ten. Write how many tens and ones.
Then write how many in all.

2 tens + 4 ones = 24 in all

$$1 \text{ tens} + 7 \text{ ones} = 17 \quad 3 \text{ tens} + 6 \text{ ones} = 36$$

$$2 \text{ tens} + 2 \text{ ones} = 22 \quad 3 \text{ tens} + 8 \text{ ones} = 38$$

$$1 \text{ tens} + 8 \text{ ones} = 18 \quad 2 \text{ tens} + 9 \text{ ones} = 29$$

56   Counting groups of tens and ones; adding

page 57

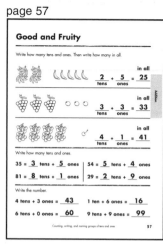

Good and Fruity

Write how many tens and ones. Then write how many in all.

$$\underline{2}_{\text{tens}} + \underline{5}_{\text{ones}} = \underline{25} \text{ in all}$$

$$\underline{3}_{\text{tens}} + \underline{3}_{\text{ones}} = \underline{33} \text{ in all}$$

$$\underline{4}_{\text{tens}} + \underline{1}_{\text{ones}} = \underline{41} \text{ in all}$$

Write how many tens and ones.

$$35 = \underline{3} \text{ tens} + \underline{5} \text{ ones} \qquad 54 = \underline{5} \text{ tens} + \underline{4} \text{ ones}$$

$$81 = \underline{8} \text{ tens} + \underline{1} \text{ ones} \qquad 29 = \underline{2} \text{ tens} + \underline{9} \text{ ones}$$

Write the number.

$$4 \text{ tens} + 3 \text{ ones} = \underline{43} \qquad 1 \text{ ten} + 6 \text{ ones} = \underline{16}$$

$$6 \text{ tens} + 0 \text{ ones} = \underline{60} \qquad 9 \text{ tens} + 9 \text{ ones} = \underline{99}$$

Counting, writing, and naming groups of tens and ones   57

page 58

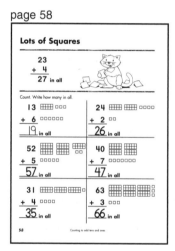

Lots of Squares

$$\begin{array}{r} 23 \\ + 4 \\ \hline 27 \end{array} \text{ in all}$$

Count. Write how many in all.

$$\begin{array}{r} 13 \\ + 6 \\ \hline 19 \end{array} \text{ in all} \qquad \begin{array}{r} 24 \\ + 2 \\ \hline 26 \end{array} \text{ in all}$$

$$\begin{array}{r} 52 \\ + 5 \\ \hline 57 \end{array} \text{ in all} \qquad \begin{array}{r} 40 \\ + 7 \\ \hline 47 \end{array} \text{ in all}$$

$$\begin{array}{r} 31 \\ + 4 \\ \hline 35 \end{array} \text{ in all} \qquad \begin{array}{r} 63 \\ + 3 \\ \hline 66 \end{array} \text{ in all}$$

58   Counting to add tens and ones

page 59

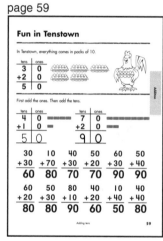

Fun in Tenstown

In Tenstown, everything comes in packs of 10.

tens	ones
3	0
+2	0
5	0

First add the ones. Then add the tens.

tens	ones		tens	ones
4	0		7	0
+1	0		+2	0
5	0		9	0

$$\begin{array}{r} 30 \\ +30 \\ \hline 60 \end{array} \begin{array}{r} 10 \\ +70 \\ \hline 80 \end{array} \begin{array}{r} 40 \\ +30 \\ \hline 70 \end{array} \begin{array}{r} 50 \\ +20 \\ \hline 70 \end{array} \begin{array}{r} 60 \\ +30 \\ \hline 90 \end{array} \begin{array}{r} 50 \\ +40 \\ \hline 90 \end{array}$$

$$\begin{array}{r} 60 \\ +20 \\ \hline 80 \end{array} \begin{array}{r} 50 \\ +30 \\ \hline 80 \end{array} \begin{array}{r} 80 \\ +10 \\ \hline 90 \end{array} \begin{array}{r} 40 \\ +20 \\ \hline 60 \end{array} \begin{array}{r} 10 \\ +40 \\ \hline 50 \end{array} \begin{array}{r} 40 \\ +40 \\ \hline 80 \end{array}$$

Adding tens   59

page 60

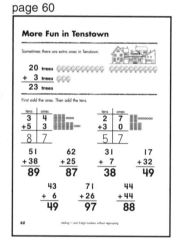

More Fun in Tenstown

Sometimes there are extra ones in Tenstown.

$$\begin{array}{r} 20 \text{ trees} \\ + 3 \text{ trees} \\ \hline 23 \text{ trees} \end{array}$$

First add the ones. Then add the tens.

tens	ones		tens	ones
3	4		2	7
+5	3		+3	0
8	7		5	7

$$\begin{array}{r} 51 \\ +38 \\ \hline 89 \end{array} \begin{array}{r} 62 \\ +25 \\ \hline 87 \end{array} \begin{array}{r} 31 \\ + 7 \\ \hline 38 \end{array} \begin{array}{r} 17 \\ +32 \\ \hline 49 \end{array}$$

$$\begin{array}{r} 43 \\ + 6 \\ \hline 49 \end{array} \begin{array}{r} 71 \\ +26 \\ \hline 97 \end{array} \begin{array}{r} 44 \\ +44 \\ \hline 88 \end{array}$$

60   Adding 1- and 2-digit numbers without regrouping

page 61

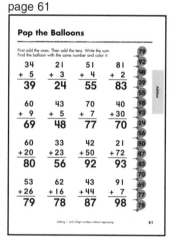

Pop the Balloons

First add the ones. Then add the tens. Write the sum.
Find the balloon with the same number and color it.

$$\begin{array}{r} 34 \\ + 5 \\ \hline 39 \end{array} \begin{array}{r} 21 \\ + 3 \\ \hline 24 \end{array} \begin{array}{r} 51 \\ + 4 \\ \hline 55 \end{array} \begin{array}{r} 81 \\ + 2 \\ \hline 83 \end{array}$$

$$\begin{array}{r} 60 \\ + 9 \\ \hline 69 \end{array} \begin{array}{r} 43 \\ + 5 \\ \hline 48 \end{array} \begin{array}{r} 70 \\ + 7 \\ \hline 77 \end{array} \begin{array}{r} 40 \\ +30 \\ \hline 70 \end{array}$$

$$\begin{array}{r} 60 \\ +20 \\ \hline 80 \end{array} \begin{array}{r} 33 \\ +23 \\ \hline 56 \end{array} \begin{array}{r} 42 \\ +50 \\ \hline 92 \end{array} \begin{array}{r} 21 \\ +72 \\ \hline 93 \end{array}$$

$$\begin{array}{r} 53 \\ +26 \\ \hline 79 \end{array} \begin{array}{r} 62 \\ +16 \\ \hline 78 \end{array} \begin{array}{r} 43 \\ +44 \\ \hline 87 \end{array} \begin{array}{r} 91 \\ + 7 \\ \hline 98 \end{array}$$

Balloons: 79, 92, 48, 39, 55, 98, 93, 56, 87, 83, 70, 69, 78

Adding 1- and 2-digit numbers without regrouping   61

page 62

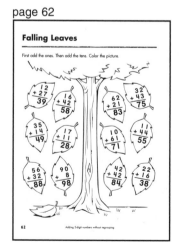

Falling Leaves

First add the ones. Then add the tens. Color the picture.

$$\begin{array}{r} 12 \\ +27 \\ \hline 39 \end{array} \quad \begin{array}{r} 16 \\ +42 \\ \hline 58 \end{array} \quad \begin{array}{r} 62 \\ +21 \\ \hline 83 \end{array} \quad \begin{array}{r} 32 \\ +43 \\ \hline 75 \end{array}$$

$$\begin{array}{r} 35 \\ +14 \\ \hline 49 \end{array} \quad \begin{array}{r} 17 \\ +11 \\ \hline 28 \end{array} \quad \begin{array}{r} 10 \\ +61 \\ \hline 71 \end{array} \quad \begin{array}{r} 11 \\ +44 \\ \hline 55 \end{array}$$

$$\begin{array}{r} 56 \\ +32 \\ \hline 88 \end{array} \quad \begin{array}{r} 90 \\ + 8 \\ \hline 98 \end{array} \quad \begin{array}{r} 42 \\ +42 \\ \hline 84 \end{array} \quad \begin{array}{r} 22 \\ +16 \\ \hline 38 \end{array}$$

62   Adding 2-digit numbers without regrouping

page 63

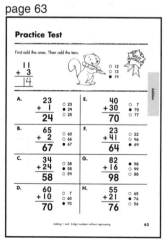

Practice Test

First add the ones. Then add the tens.

$$\begin{array}{r} 11 \\ + 3 \\ \hline 14 \end{array}$$
○ 12   ○ 13   ● 14

A.
$$\begin{array}{r} 23 \\ + 1 \\ \hline 24 \end{array}$$
○ 23   ● 24   ○ 25

B.
$$\begin{array}{r} 65 \\ + 2 \\ \hline 67 \end{array}$$
○ 60   ○ 66   ● 67

C.
$$\begin{array}{r} 34 \\ +24 \\ \hline 58 \end{array}$$
○ 38   ● 58   ○ 54

D.
$$\begin{array}{r} 60 \\ +10 \\ \hline 70 \end{array}$$
○ 7   ○ 60   ● 70

E.
$$\begin{array}{r} 40 \\ +30 \\ \hline 70 \end{array}$$
○ 7   ● 70   ○ 77

F.
$$\begin{array}{r} 23 \\ +41 \\ \hline 64 \end{array}$$
○ 22   ○ 46   ● 64

G.
$$\begin{array}{r} 82 \\ +16 \\ \hline 98 \end{array}$$
● 98   ○ 99   ○ 88

H.
$$\begin{array}{r} 55 \\ +21 \\ \hline 76 \end{array}$$
○ 65   ● 76   ○ 56

Adding 1- and 2-digit numbers without regrouping   63

Hats Off

Subtract.

How many are left? $5 - 3 =$ _____ 2

How many are left? $5 - 4 =$ _____

How many are left? $3 - 1 =$ _____

Subtraction

How many are left? $4 - 3 =$ _____

Color the answer.

What has a head and a foot, but no body?

On Your Feet

Cross out and subtract.

X out 1.

How many are left?   4 – 1 = _____ 3

X out 4.

How many are left?   5 – 4 = _____

X out 2.

How many are left?   2 – 2 = _____

X out 3.

How many are left?   4 – 3 = _____

Color the answer.

What has two hands but no feet?

Subtracting numbers 0-5 from numbers to 5

In the Kitchen

Subtract.

How many are left? **8 − 4 = ____**

How many are left? **8 − 3 = ____**

How many are left? **7 − 6 = ____**

How many are left? **7 − 2 = ____**

Circle the answer.

There are 7 s of .
Oops! Somebody spilled 5.
How many s are left?

3 2

Subtraction

Keys, Please

Cross out and subtract.

X out 6.

How many are left? 8 − 6 = ____2____

X out 5.

How many are left? 8 − 5 = _____

X out 3.

How many are left? 7 − 3 = _____

X out 6.

How many are left? 7 − 6 = _____

X out 2.

How many are left? 8 − 2 = _____

Subtracting numbers 0-8 from numbers to 8

Top to Bottom

Subtract.

$$\begin{array}{r} 8 \\ -\ 5 \\ \hline \end{array}$$

How many are left? ____

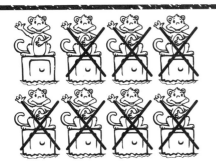

$$\begin{array}{r} 8 \\ -\ 7 \\ \hline \end{array}$$

How many are left? ____

$$\begin{array}{r} 8 \\ -\ 6 \\ \hline \end{array}$$

How many are left? ____

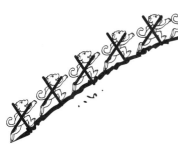

$$\begin{array}{r} 7 \\ -\ 5 \\ \hline \end{array}$$

How many are left? ____

$$\begin{array}{r} 7 \\ -\ 4 \\ \hline \end{array}$$

How many are left? ____

$$\begin{array}{r} 8 \\ -\ 4 \\ \hline \end{array}$$

How many are left? ____

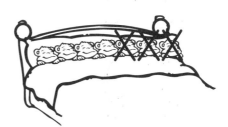

$$\begin{array}{r} 7 \\ -\ 3 \\ \hline \end{array}$$

How many are left? ____

Subtracting numbers through 8 in vertical form

Who's There?

Subtract. Color the spaces to match the answers in the code.

2 = orange	4 = green
3 = blue	5 = yellow

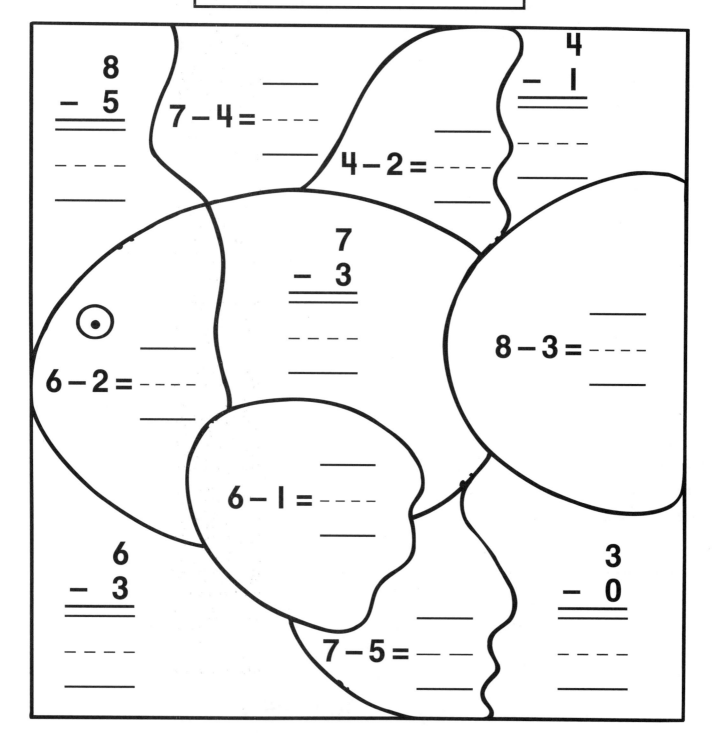

$$\begin{array}{r} 8 \\ -\ 5 \\ \hline \end{array}$$

$7 - 4 =$ ----

$4 - 2 =$ ----

$$\begin{array}{r} 4 \\ -\ 1 \\ \hline \end{array}$$

$$\begin{array}{r} 7 \\ -\ 3 \\ \hline \end{array}$$

$8 - 3 =$ ----

$6 - 2 =$ ----

$6 - 1 =$ ----

$$\begin{array}{r} 6 \\ -\ 3 \\ \hline \end{array}$$

$7 - 5 =$ ---

$$\begin{array}{r} 3 \\ -\ 0 \\ \hline \end{array}$$

Reviewing subtraction facts to 8

Color Away

Subtract.

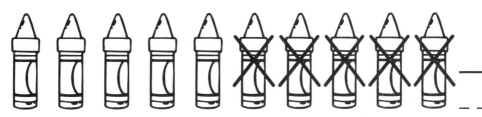

How many are left? **10 − 5 =** _____

How many are left? **10 − 6 =** _____

How many are left? **9 − 5 =** _____

How many are left? **8 − 6 =** _____

How many are left? **9 − 3 =** _____

Subtracting numbers 0-10 from numbers to 10

Make Music

Cross out and subtract.

X out 7.

How many are left? 10 − 7 = _____ 3

X out 7.

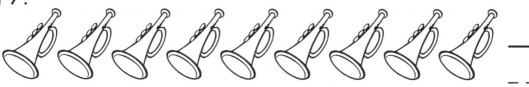

How many are left? 9 − 7 = _____

X out 8.

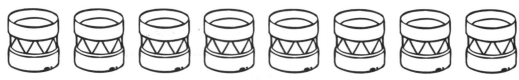

How many are left? 8 − 8 = _____

X out 5.

How many are left? 10 − 5 = _____

Write the answer.

10 🔔**s rang so fine.**

_____

1 fell. **Now there are** _____

Fresh Fruit

Cross out and subtract.

$$\begin{array}{r} 10 \\ -4 \\ \hline \end{array}$$

How many are left? _6_

X out 6.

$$\begin{array}{r} 9 \\ -6 \\ \hline \end{array}$$

How many are left? _____

X out 3.

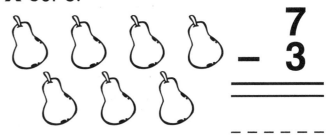

$$\begin{array}{r} 7 \\ -3 \\ \hline \end{array}$$

How many are left? _____

X out 6.

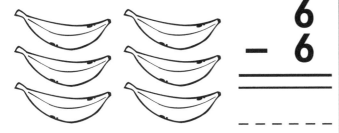

$$\begin{array}{r} 6 \\ -6 \\ \hline \end{array}$$

How many are left? _____

X out 2.

$$\begin{array}{r} 10 \\ -2 \\ \hline \end{array}$$

How many are left? _____

Subtraction

Color the answer.

What has a mouth but cannot talk?

Subtraction Stories

Write the answer.

Five s. Four blow away.

How many are left?   5 – 4 = _____

Nine s. Three go out.

How many are left?   9 – 3 = _____

Ten s. Seven get picked.

How many are left?   10 – 7 = _____

Eight s. Four are eaten.

How many are left?   8 – 4 = _____

Seven s. Two crawl away.

How many are left?   7 – 2 = _____

Check It!

Subtract. Then add to check.

5 − 3 = **2**  ✔ 2 + 3 = **5**

9 − 5  = _____ ✔ 4 + 5 = _____

6 − 4  = _____ ✔ 2 + 4 = _____

10 − 3  = _____ ✔ 7 + 3 = _____

9 − 6  = _____ ✔ 3 + 6 = _____

Party Time

Write how many are left.

How many are left?

$14 - 8 =$ _____ 6

$13 - 6 =$ _____

$12 - 7 =$ _____

$9 - 0 =$ _____

$11 - 5 =$ _____

Subtracting numbers 0-9 from numbers through 14

Home Sweet Home

Cross out and subtract. Write how many are left.

How many are left?

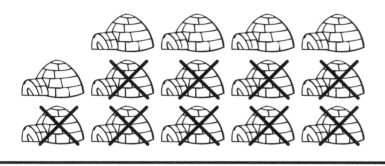

$14 - 9 =$ _____

$10 - 7 =$ _____

$12 - 6 =$ _____

$13 - 5 =$ _____

Subtraction

Color the answer.

What animal never leaves home?

Down We Go

Cross out and subtract. Write how many are left.

$$\begin{array}{r} 11 \\ -5 \\ \hline \end{array}$$

6

$$\begin{array}{r} 14 \\ -6 \\ \hline \end{array}$$

$$\begin{array}{r} 13 \\ -4 \\ \hline \end{array}$$

$$\begin{array}{r} 12 \\ -8 \\ \hline \end{array}$$

$$\begin{array}{r} 11 \\ -9 \\ \hline \end{array}$$

Write the missing numbers.

14, 12, _____, 8, _____, 4, 2

Subtracting numbers 0-9 from numbers through 14 in vertical form

Have a Nice Trip

Cross out and subtract. Write how many are left.

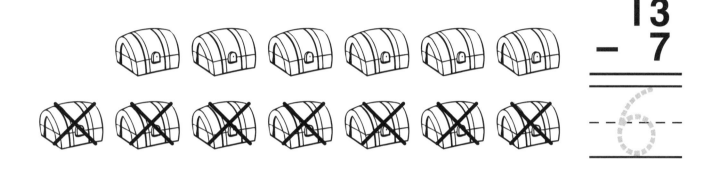

$$\begin{array}{r} 13 \\ -\ 7 \\ \hline \end{array}$$

6

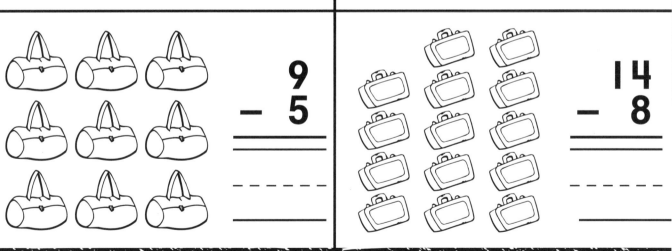

$$\begin{array}{r} 12 \\ -\ 3 \\ \hline \end{array}$$

$$\begin{array}{r} 11 \\ -\ 6 \\ \hline \end{array}$$

$$\begin{array}{r} 9 \\ -\ 5 \\ \hline \end{array}$$

$$\begin{array}{r} 14 \\ -\ 8 \\ \hline \end{array}$$

Subtraction

Circle the answer.

What can travel all over but never leaves the corner?

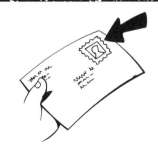

Subtracting numbers 0-9 from numbers through 14 in vertical form

81

Review

Subtract.

$$\begin{array}{r} 10 \\ -\ 7 \\ \hline \end{array}$$ $$\begin{array}{r} 11 \\ -\ 6 \\ \hline \end{array}$$ $$\begin{array}{r} 14 \\ -\ 5 \\ \hline \end{array}$$ $$\begin{array}{r} 13 \\ -\ 3 \\ \hline \end{array}$$

$$\begin{array}{r} 12 \\ -\ 9 \\ \hline \end{array}$$ $$\begin{array}{r} 10 \\ -\ 5 \\ \hline \end{array}$$ $$\begin{array}{r} 9 \\ -\ 7 \\ \hline \end{array}$$ $$\begin{array}{r} 13 \\ -\ 6 \\ \hline \end{array}$$ $$\begin{array}{r} 11 \\ -\ 7 \\ \hline \end{array}$$

$$\begin{array}{r} 10 \\ -\ 6 \\ \hline \end{array}$$ $$\begin{array}{r} 14 \\ -\ 8 \\ \hline \end{array}$$ $$\begin{array}{r} 8 \\ -\ 6 \\ \hline \end{array}$$ $$\begin{array}{r} 12 \\ -\ 6 \\ \hline \end{array}$$ $$\begin{array}{r} 13 \\ -\ 5 \\ \hline \end{array}$$

$$\begin{array}{r} 11 \\ -\ 2 \\ \hline \end{array}$$ $$\begin{array}{r} 12 \\ -\ 4 \\ \hline \end{array}$$ $$\begin{array}{r} 14 \\ -\ 6 \\ \hline \end{array}$$ $$\begin{array}{r} 12 \\ -\ 8 \\ \hline \end{array}$$ $$\begin{array}{r} 13 \\ -\ 7 \\ \hline \end{array}$$

Reviewing subtraction facts through 14

I Need Some More

Subtract.
Write how many more are
needed to make 10.

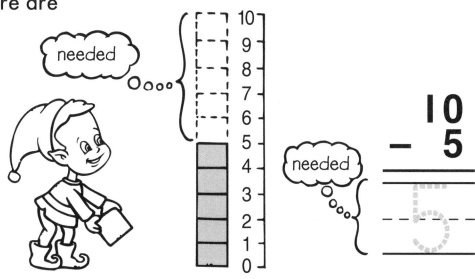

$$10 - 5$$

$$10 - 7$$

$$10 - 6$$

Color the correct answer box.

 has 8  **s.**

He wants 10  **s.**

How many more  **s does** **need?**

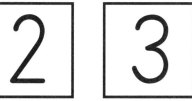

2   3

Nuts and Bolts

Subtract. Write how many are left.

How many are left? 15 − 8 = _____ 7

14 − 9 = _____

11 − 8 = _____

18 − 9 = _____

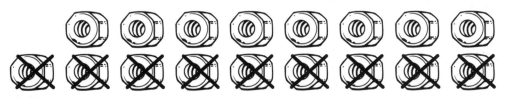

17 − 9 = _____

Subtracting numbers 0-9 from numbers through 18

Too Many Tools

Cross out and subtract. Write how many are left.

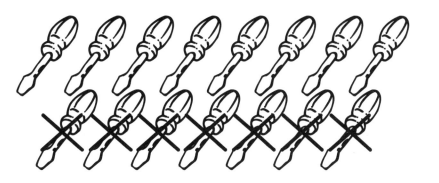

$$\begin{array}{r} 15 \\ -\ 7 \\ \hline \end{array}$$

8

How many are left? _____

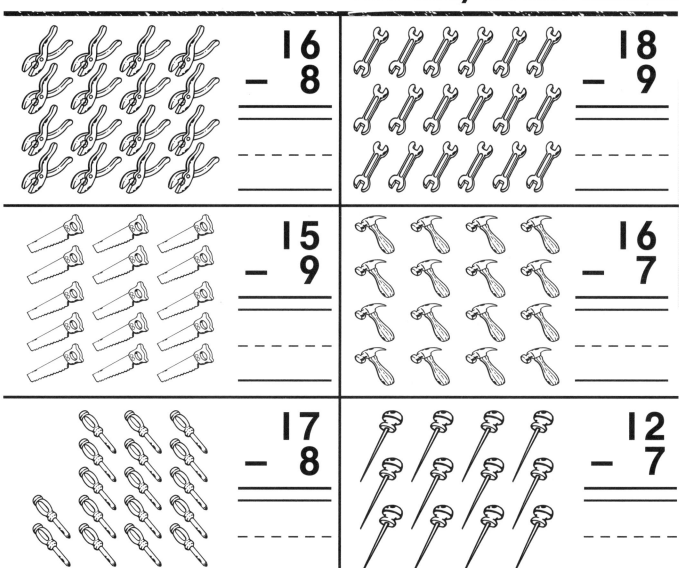

$$\begin{array}{r} 16 \\ -\ 8 \\ \hline \end{array}$$

$$\begin{array}{r} 18 \\ -\ 9 \\ \hline \end{array}$$

$$\begin{array}{r} 15 \\ -\ 9 \\ \hline \end{array}$$

$$\begin{array}{r} 16 \\ -\ 7 \\ \hline \end{array}$$

$$\begin{array}{r} 17 \\ -\ 8 \\ \hline \end{array}$$

$$\begin{array}{r} 12 \\ -\ 7 \\ \hline \end{array}$$

Subtracting numbers 0-9 from numbers through 18 in vertical form

Zoom Along

Cross out and subtract. Write how many are left.

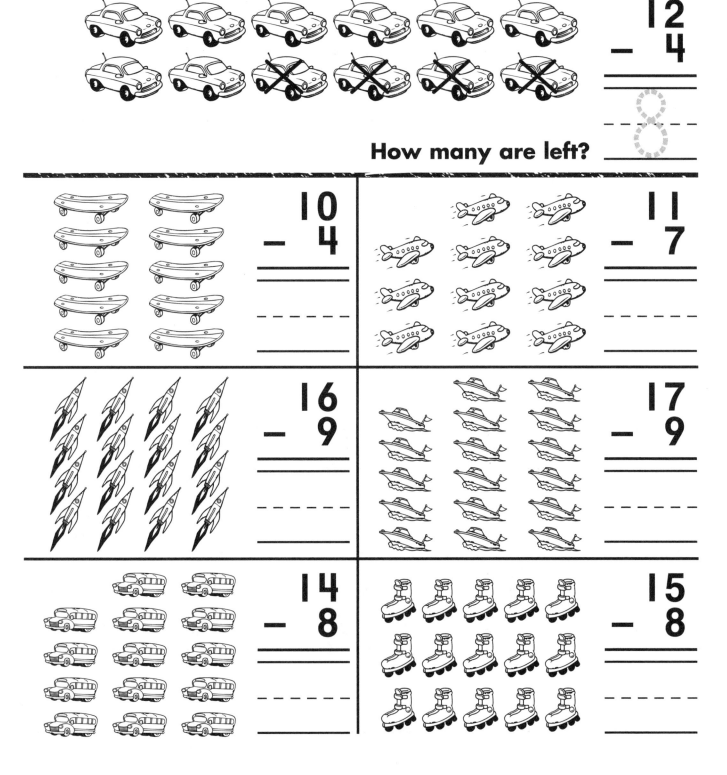

$$\begin{array}{r} 12 \\ -4 \\ \hline \end{array}$$

8

How many are left? _____

$$\begin{array}{r} 10 \\ -4 \\ \hline \end{array}$$

$$\begin{array}{r} 11 \\ -7 \\ \hline \end{array}$$

$$\begin{array}{r} 16 \\ -9 \\ \hline \end{array}$$

$$\begin{array}{r} 17 \\ -9 \\ \hline \end{array}$$

$$\begin{array}{r} 14 \\ -8 \\ \hline \end{array}$$

$$\begin{array}{r} 15 \\ -8 \\ \hline \end{array}$$

Subtracting numbers 0-9 from numbers through 18 in vertical form

Review

Subtract.

10 − 7	12 − 6	18 − 9	16 − 7	12 − 8

15 − 7	13 − 9	17 − 8	11 − 8	14 − 6

13 − 5	11 − 6	15 − 8	16 − 9	

13 − 7	15 − 9	17 − 9	16 − 8	12 − 7

Tens Take Away

Cross out groups of ten.
First subtract the ones column.
Then subtract the tens column.

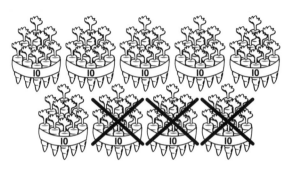

tens	ones
9	0
−3	0
6	0

How many are left? _____

tens	ones		tens	ones
8	0		7	0
−4	0		−5	0

First subtract the ones.
Then subtract the tens.

80	60	50
−30	−20	−40

40	60	90	30	50
−10	−30	−80	−20	−20

You Can Do It!

First subtract the ones. Then subtract the tens.

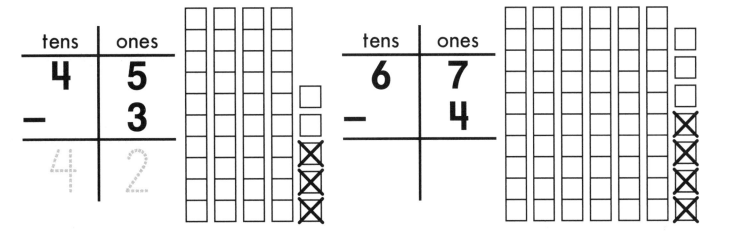

tens	ones
3	6
−	3

tens	ones
6	8
−	5

tens	ones
7	2
−	1

tens	ones
5	7
−	6

tens	ones
3	9
−	8

tens	ones
5	5
−	3

tens	ones
9	8
−	8

tens	ones
6	9
−	5

Subtraction

Brush Off

Subtract the ones. Write how many are left.

tens	ones
3	5
−	3
3	2

   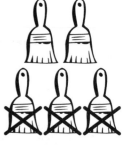

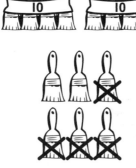

tens	ones
2	6
−	4

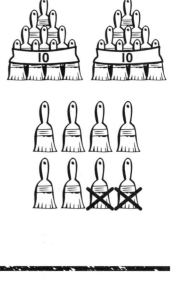

tens	ones
4	8
−	2

$$87 - 6$$ $$54 - 1$$ $$63 - 3$$ $$99 - 4$$ $$75 - 2$$

$$49 - 7$$ $$68 - 4$$ $$96 - 2$$ $$36 - 5$$ $$55 - 3$$

Subtracting 1-digit numbers from 2-digit numbers without regrouping

Practice Makes Purr-fect

Color the spaces to match the
answers in the code.

8 = yellow	20 = red
12 = orange	30 = green

Practice Test

$$\begin{array}{r} 40 \\ -20 \\ \hline 20 \end{array}$$

- ○ 30
- ● 20
- ○ 10

A.
$$\begin{array}{r} 60 \\ -20 \\ \hline \end{array}$$
- ○ 60
- ○ 50
- ○ 40

E.
$$\begin{array}{r} 89 \\ -9 \\ \hline \end{array}$$
- ○ 90
- ○ 81
- ○ 80

B.
$$\begin{array}{r} 37 \\ -5 \\ \hline \end{array}$$
- ○ 32
- ○ 31
- ○ 30

F.
$$\begin{array}{r} 64 \\ -1 \\ \hline \end{array}$$
- ○ 68
- ○ 65
- ○ 63

C.
$$\begin{array}{r} 54 \\ -3 \\ \hline \end{array}$$
- ○ 52
- ○ 51
- ○ 50

G.
$$\begin{array}{r} 38 \\ -7 \\ \hline \end{array}$$
- ○ 32
- ○ 31
- ○ 30

D.
$$\begin{array}{r} 78 \\ -3 \\ \hline \end{array}$$
- ○ 76
- ○ 75
- ○ 74

H.
$$\begin{array}{r} 90 \\ -70 \\ \hline \end{array}$$
- ○ 30
- ○ 20
- ○ 10

Detect the Difference

Subtract, then circle the number that matches your answer.

```
  57          40
-  2        - 10
```
59 (55)   20 30

```
  91          68
-  0        -  6
```
91 90   64 62

```
  70          10          84          99
- 20        - 10        -  3        -  3
```
50 90   10   0   82 81   96 95

```
  78          60          58          90
-  5        - 10        -  2        - 60
```
74 73   50 70   54 56   20 30

Subtraction

Winning Scores

Circle the greater score. Subtract to find out by how many points the home team won.

HOME	8
VISITOR	4

HOME	23
VISITOR	0

HOME	18
VISITOR	9

HOME	15
VISITOR	5

HOME	17
VISITOR	8

HOME	75
VISITOR	5

HOME	36
VISITOR	2

HOME	27
VISITOR	3

HOME	14
VISITOR	7

Subtraction review

Answer Key

As the child completes the pages in this section, review his or her answers. When you take the time to correct the work and explain mistakes, you're showing your child that you feel learning is important.

page 67

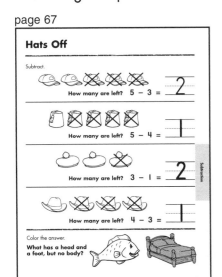

page 68

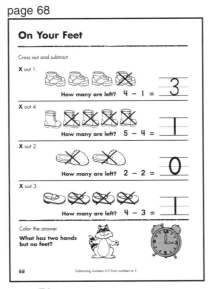

page 69

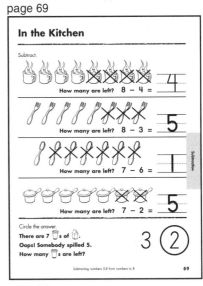

page 70

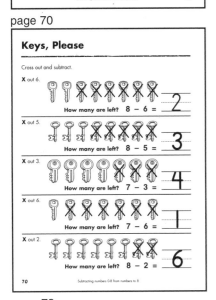

page 71

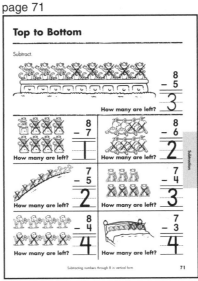

page 72

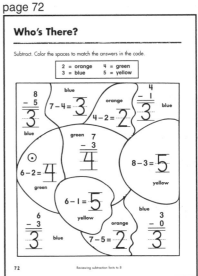

page 73

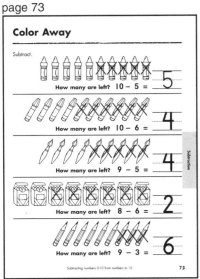

page 74

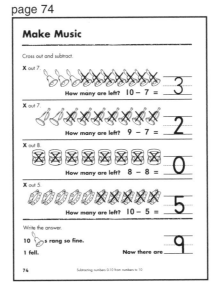

page 75

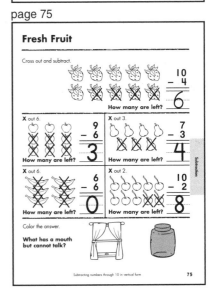

page 76

Subtraction Stories

Write the answer.

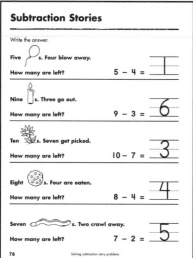

Five 🎈 s. Four blow away.

How many are left? 5 − 4 = **1**

Nine 🕯 s. Three go out.

How many are left? 9 − 3 = **6**

Ten 🌿 s. Seven get picked.

How many are left? 10 − 7 = **3**

Eight 🍪 s. Four are eaten.

How many are left? 8 − 4 = **4**

Seven 🐛 s. Two crawl away.

How many are left? 7 − 2 = **5**

76   Solving subtraction story problems

page 77

Check It!

Subtract. Then add to check.

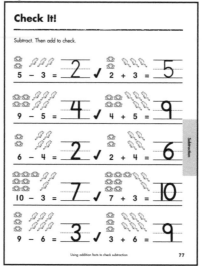

5 − 3 = **2** ✓ 2 + 3 = **5**

9 − 5 = **4** ✓ 4 + 5 = **9**

6 − 4 = **2** ✓ 2 + 4 = **6**

10 − 3 = **7** ✓ 7 + 3 = **10**

9 − 6 = **3** ✓ 3 + 6 = **9**

Using addition facts to check subtraction   77

page 78

Party Time

Write how many are left.

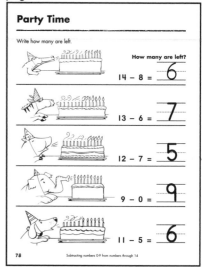

How many are left?

14 − 8 = **6**

13 − 6 = **7**

12 − 7 = **5**

9 − 0 = **9**

11 − 5 = **6**

78   Subtracting numbers 0-9 from numbers through 14

page 79

Home Sweet Home

Cross out and subtract. Write how many are left.

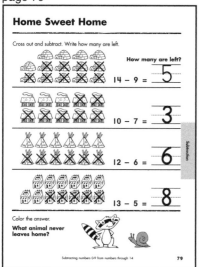

How many are left?

14 − 9 = **5**

10 − 7 = **3**

12 − 6 = **6**

13 − 5 = **8**

Color the answer.

What animal never leaves home?

Subtracting numbers 0-9 from numbers through 14   79

page 80

Down We Go

Cross out and subtract. Write how many are left.

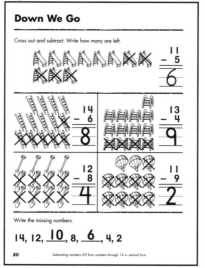

$\begin{array}{r} 11 \\ -\ 5 \\ \hline 6 \end{array}$

$\begin{array}{r} 14 \\ -\ 6 \\ \hline 8 \end{array}$

$\begin{array}{r} 13 \\ -\ 4 \\ \hline 9 \end{array}$

$\begin{array}{r} 12 \\ -\ 8 \\ \hline 4 \end{array}$

$\begin{array}{r} 11 \\ -\ 9 \\ \hline 2 \end{array}$

Write the missing numbers.

14, 12, **10**, 8, **6**, 4, 2

80   Subtracting numbers 0-9 from numbers through 14 in vertical form

page 81

Have a Nice Trip

Cross out and subtract. Write how many are left.

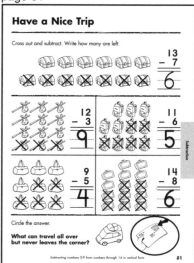

$\begin{array}{r} 13 \\ -\ 7 \\ \hline 6 \end{array}$

$\begin{array}{r} 12 \\ -\ 3 \\ \hline 9 \end{array}$

$\begin{array}{r} 11 \\ -\ 6 \\ \hline 5 \end{array}$

$\begin{array}{r} 9 \\ -\ 5 \\ \hline 4 \end{array}$

$\begin{array}{r} 14 \\ -\ 8 \\ \hline 6 \end{array}$

Circle the answer.

What can travel all over but never leaves the corner?

Subtracting numbers 0-9 from numbers through 14 in vertical form   81

page 82

Review

Subtract.

$\begin{array}{r} 10 \\ -\ 7 \\ \hline 3 \end{array}$ $\begin{array}{r} 11 \\ -\ 6 \\ \hline 5 \end{array}$ $\begin{array}{r} 14 \\ -\ 5 \\ \hline 9 \end{array}$ $\begin{array}{r} 13 \\ -\ 3 \\ \hline 10 \end{array}$

$\begin{array}{r} 12 \\ -\ 9 \\ \hline 3 \end{array}$ $\begin{array}{r} 10 \\ -\ 5 \\ \hline 5 \end{array}$ $\begin{array}{r} 9 \\ -\ 7 \\ \hline 2 \end{array}$ $\begin{array}{r} 13 \\ -\ 6 \\ \hline 7 \end{array}$ $\begin{array}{r} 11 \\ -\ 7 \\ \hline 4 \end{array}$

$\begin{array}{r} 10 \\ -\ 6 \\ \hline 4 \end{array}$ $\begin{array}{r} 14 \\ -\ 8 \\ \hline 6 \end{array}$ $\begin{array}{r} 8 \\ -\ 6 \\ \hline 2 \end{array}$ $\begin{array}{r} 12 \\ -\ 6 \\ \hline 6 \end{array}$ $\begin{array}{r} 13 \\ -\ 5 \\ \hline 8 \end{array}$

$\begin{array}{r} 11 \\ -\ 2 \\ \hline 9 \end{array}$ $\begin{array}{r} 12 \\ -\ 4 \\ \hline 8 \end{array}$ $\begin{array}{r} 14 \\ -\ 6 \\ \hline 8 \end{array}$ $\begin{array}{r} 12 \\ -\ 8 \\ \hline 4 \end{array}$ $\begin{array}{r} 13 \\ -\ 7 \\ \hline 6 \end{array}$

82   Reviewing subtraction facts through 14

page 83

I Need Some More

Subtract.
Write how many more are **needed** to make 10.

$\begin{array}{r} 10 \\ -\ 5 \\ \hline 5 \end{array}$

$\begin{array}{r} 10 \\ -\ 7 \\ \hline 3 \end{array}$

$\begin{array}{r} 10 \\ -\ 6 \\ \hline 4 \end{array}$

Color the correct answer box.

🐦 has 8 🐦 s.

He wants 10 🐦 s.

How many more 🐦 s does 🐦 need?   **2** [3]

Using subtraction to find out how many more are needed   83

page 84

Nuts and Bolts

Subtract. Write how many are left.

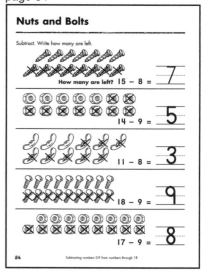

How many are left? 15 − 8 = **7**

14 − 9 = **5**

11 − 8 = **3**

18 − 9 = **9**

17 − 9 = **8**

84   Subtracting numbers 0-9 from numbers through 18

page 85

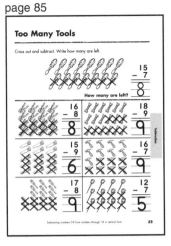

Too Many Tools

Cross out and subtract. Write how many are left.

$\begin{array}{r} 15 \\ -\ 7 \\ \hline 8 \end{array}$

How many are left?

$\begin{array}{r} 16 \\ -\ 8 \\ \hline 8 \end{array}$ $\begin{array}{r} 18 \\ -\ 9 \\ \hline 9 \end{array}$

$\begin{array}{r} 15 \\ -\ 9 \\ \hline 6 \end{array}$ $\begin{array}{r} 16 \\ -\ 7 \\ \hline 9 \end{array}$

$\begin{array}{r} 17 \\ -\ 8 \\ \hline 9 \end{array}$ $\begin{array}{r} 12 \\ -\ 7 \\ \hline 5 \end{array}$

Subtracting numbers 0-9 from numbers through 18 in vertical form   85

page 86

Zoom Along

Cross out and subtract. Write how many are left.

$\begin{array}{r} 12 \\ -\ 4 \\ \hline 8 \end{array}$

How many are left?

$\begin{array}{r} 10 \\ -\ 4 \\ \hline 6 \end{array}$ $\begin{array}{r} 11 \\ -\ 7 \\ \hline 4 \end{array}$

$\begin{array}{r} 16 \\ -\ 9 \\ \hline 7 \end{array}$ $\begin{array}{r} 17 \\ -\ 9 \\ \hline 8 \end{array}$

$\begin{array}{r} 14 \\ -\ 8 \\ \hline 6 \end{array}$ $\begin{array}{r} 15 \\ -\ 7 \\ \hline 8 \end{array}$

86   Subtracting numbers 0-9 from numbers through 18 in vertical form

page 87

Review

Subtract.

$\begin{array}{r} 10 \\ -\ 7 \\ \hline 3 \end{array}$ $\begin{array}{r} 12 \\ -\ 6 \\ \hline 6 \end{array}$ $\begin{array}{r} 18 \\ -\ 9 \\ \hline 9 \end{array}$ $\begin{array}{r} 16 \\ -\ 7 \\ \hline 9 \end{array}$ $\begin{array}{r} 12 \\ -\ 8 \\ \hline 4 \end{array}$

$\begin{array}{r} 15 \\ -\ 7 \\ \hline 8 \end{array}$ $\begin{array}{r} 13 \\ -\ 9 \\ \hline 4 \end{array}$ $\begin{array}{r} 17 \\ -\ 8 \\ \hline 9 \end{array}$ $\begin{array}{r} 11 \\ -\ 8 \\ \hline 3 \end{array}$ $\begin{array}{r} 14 \\ -\ 6 \\ \hline 8 \end{array}$

$\begin{array}{r} 13 \\ -\ 5 \\ \hline 8 \end{array}$ $\begin{array}{r} 11 \\ -\ 6 \\ \hline 5 \end{array}$ $\begin{array}{r} 15 \\ -\ 9 \\ \hline 7 \end{array}$ $\begin{array}{r} 16 \\ -\ 9 \\ \hline 7 \end{array}$

$\begin{array}{r} 13 \\ -\ 7 \\ \hline 6 \end{array}$ $\begin{array}{r} 15 \\ -\ 9 \\ \hline 6 \end{array}$ $\begin{array}{r} 17 \\ -\ 9 \\ \hline 8 \end{array}$ $\begin{array}{r} 16 \\ -\ 8 \\ \hline 8 \end{array}$ $\begin{array}{r} 12 \\ -\ 7 \\ \hline 5 \end{array}$

Reviewing subtraction facts through 18   87

page 88

Tens Take Away

Cross out groups of ten.
First subtract the ones column.
Then subtract the tens column.

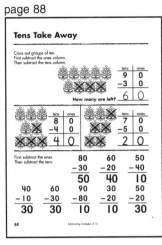

tens	ones
9	0
-3	0
6	0

How many are left?

tens	ones
8	0
-4	0
4	0

tens	ones
7	0
-5	0
2	0

First subtract the ones.
Then subtract the tens.

$\begin{array}{r} 80 \\ -30 \\ \hline 50 \end{array}$ $\begin{array}{r} 60 \\ -20 \\ \hline 40 \end{array}$ $\begin{array}{r} 50 \\ -40 \\ \hline 10 \end{array}$

$\begin{array}{r} 40 \\ -10 \\ \hline 30 \end{array}$ $\begin{array}{r} 60 \\ -30 \\ \hline 30 \end{array}$ $\begin{array}{r} 90 \\ -80 \\ \hline 10 \end{array}$ $\begin{array}{r} 30 \\ -20 \\ \hline 10 \end{array}$ $\begin{array}{r} 50 \\ -20 \\ \hline 30 \end{array}$

88   Subtracting multiples of 10

page 89

You Can Do It!

First subtract the ones. Then subtract the tens.

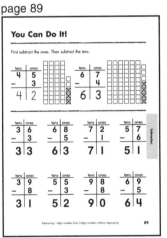

tens	ones
4	5
-	3
4	2

tens	ones
6	7
-	4
6	3

tens	ones
3	6
-	3
3	3

tens	ones
6	8
-	5
6	3

tens	ones
7	2
-	1
7	1

tens	ones
5	7
-	6
5	1

tens	ones
3	9
-	8
3	1

tens	ones
5	5
-	3
5	2

tens	ones
9	8
-	8
9	0

tens	ones
6	9
-	5
6	4

Subtracting 1-digit numbers from 2-digit numbers without regrouping   89

page 90

Brush Off

Subtract the ones. Write how many are left.

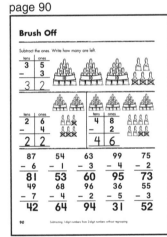

tens	ones
3	5
-	3
3	2

tens	ones
2	4
-	2
2	2

tens	ones
4	8
-	2
4	6

$\begin{array}{r} 87 \\ -\ 6 \\ \hline 81 \end{array}$ $\begin{array}{r} 54 \\ -\ 1 \\ \hline 53 \end{array}$ $\begin{array}{r} 63 \\ -\ 3 \\ \hline 60 \end{array}$ $\begin{array}{r} 99 \\ -\ 4 \\ \hline 95 \end{array}$ $\begin{array}{r} 75 \\ -\ 2 \\ \hline 73 \end{array}$

$\begin{array}{r} 49 \\ -\ 7 \\ \hline 42 \end{array}$ $\begin{array}{r} 68 \\ -\ 4 \\ \hline 64 \end{array}$ $\begin{array}{r} 96 \\ -\ 2 \\ \hline 94 \end{array}$ $\begin{array}{r} 36 \\ -\ 5 \\ \hline 31 \end{array}$ $\begin{array}{r} 55 \\ -\ 3 \\ \hline 52 \end{array}$

90   Subtracting 1-digit numbers from 2-digit numbers without regrouping

page 91

Practice Makes Purr-fect

Color the spaces to match the
answers in the code.

8 = yellow   20 = red
12 = orange   30 = green

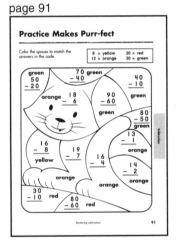

green
$\begin{array}{r} 50 \\ -20 \end{array}$

$\begin{array}{r} 70 \\ -40 \end{array}$ green

$\begin{array}{r} 40 \\ -10 \end{array}$ green

orange $\begin{array}{r} 1\ 8 \\ -\ 6 \end{array}$

$\begin{array}{r} 90 \\ -60 \end{array}$ green

$\begin{array}{r} 80 \\ -50 \end{array}$ green

$\begin{array}{r} 1\ 6 \\ -\ 8 \end{array}$ $\begin{array}{r} 1\ 9 \\ -\ 7 \end{array}$ $\begin{array}{r} 1\ 6 \\ -\ 4 \end{array}$

yellow

$\begin{array}{r} 1\ 3 \\ -\ 1 \end{array}$ orange

$\begin{array}{r} 1\ 4 \\ -\ 2 \end{array}$ orange

orange

$\begin{array}{r} 30 \\ -10 \end{array}$ red $\begin{array}{r} 80 \\ -60 \end{array}$ red

Reviewing subtraction   91

page 92

Practice Test

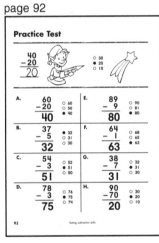

$\begin{array}{r} 40 \\ -20 \\ \hline 20 \end{array}$

○ 30
● 20
○ 10

A. $\begin{array}{r} 60 \\ -20 \\ \hline 40 \end{array}$ ○ 32 ○ 50 ● 40

E. $\begin{array}{r} 89 \\ -\ 9 \\ \hline 80 \end{array}$ ○ 90 ○ 81 ● 80

B. $\begin{array}{r} 37 \\ -\ 5 \\ \hline 32 \end{array}$ ● 32 ○ 31 ○ 30

F. $\begin{array}{r} 64 \\ -\ 1 \\ \hline 63 \end{array}$ ○ 68 ○ 65 ● 63

C. $\begin{array}{r} 54 \\ -\ 3 \\ \hline 51 \end{array}$ ○ 52 ● 51 ○ 50

G. $\begin{array}{r} 38 \\ -\ 7 \\ \hline 31 \end{array}$ ○ 32 ● 31 ○ 30

D. $\begin{array}{r} 78 \\ -\ 3 \\ \hline 75 \end{array}$ ○ 76 ● 75 ○ 74

H. $\begin{array}{r} 90 \\ -70 \\ \hline 20 \end{array}$ ○ 30 ● 20 ○ 10

92   Testing subtraction skills

page 93

Detect the Difference

Subtract, then circle the number that matches your answer.

$\begin{array}{r} 57 \\ -\ 2 \end{array}$ 59 (55)

$\begin{array}{r} 40 \\ -10 \end{array}$ 20 (30)

$\begin{array}{r} 91 \\ -\ 0 \end{array}$ (91) 90

$\begin{array}{r} 68 \\ -\ 6 \end{array}$ 64 (62)

$\begin{array}{r} 70 \\ -20 \end{array}$ (50) 90

$\begin{array}{r} 10 \\ -10 \end{array}$ 10 (0)

$\begin{array}{r} 84 \\ -\ 3 \end{array}$ 82 (81)

$\begin{array}{r} 99 \\ -\ 3 \end{array}$ (96) 95

$\begin{array}{r} 78 \\ -\ 5 \end{array}$ 74 (73)

$\begin{array}{r} 60 \\ -10 \end{array}$ (50) 70

$\begin{array}{r} 58 \\ -\ 2 \end{array}$ 54 (56)

$\begin{array}{r} 90 \\ -60 \end{array}$ 20 (30)

Subtracting 1-digit numbers from 2-digit numbers without regrouping   93

page 94

Winning Scores

Circle the greater score. Subtract to find out
by how many points the home team won.

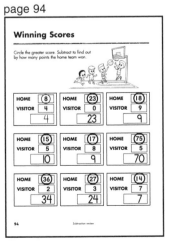

HOME (8)	HOME (23)	HOME (18)
VISITOR 4	VISITOR 0	VISITOR 9
4	23	9

HOME (15)	HOME (17)	HOME (75)
VISITOR 5	VISITOR 8	VISITOR 5
10	9	70

HOME (36)	HOME (27)	HOME (14)
VISITOR 2	VISITOR 3	VISITOR 7
34	24	7

94   Subtraction review

Count and Color

Count the shapes. Write how many.

How many ⬜s? _ _ _ _ _ _ _
Color them red. _____

How many △s? _ _ _ _ _ _ _
Color them green. _____

How many ◯s? _ _ _ _ _ _ _
Color them blue. _____

How many ▭s? _ _ _ _ _ _ _
Color them yellow. _____

Identifying and counting shapes

Graph It!

Color the graph to show how many of each shape is on page 98.

10				
9				
8				
7				
6				
5				
4				
3				
2				
1				

□　　○　　△　　▭

Math Concepts

Garden Graph

Count how many the rabbit picked.
Color the graph to show the number of each.

9					
8					
7					
6					
5					
4					
3					
2					
1					

Completing a graph

What's Next?

Draw the shape that comes next.
Color each pattern using the code.

○ = blue   △ = red

▢ = green   ▭ = yellow

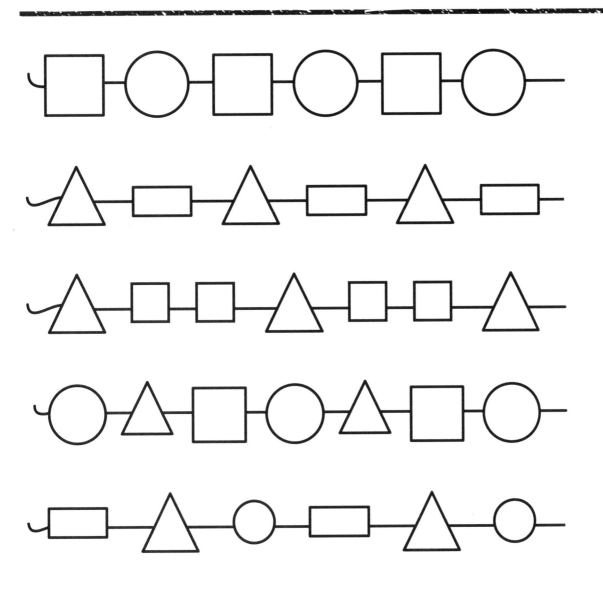

Math Concepts

Recognizing and completing shape patterns   **101**

What's Missing?

Draw the missing shapes. Then color each row of shapes to make your own patterns.

Recognizing and completing shape patterns

Shape Puzzlers

Look closely. How many triangles do you see? Write the number.

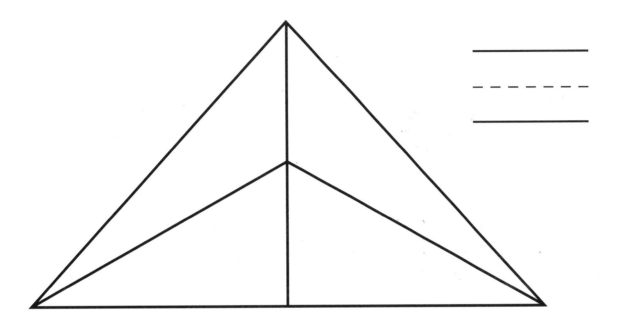

Look closely. How many rectangles do you see? Write the number.

Math Concepts

Shape Search

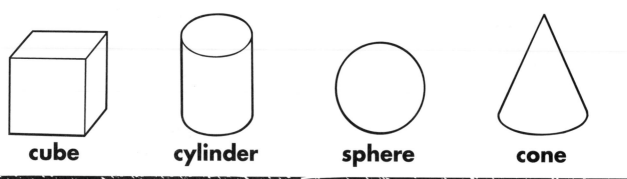

| cube | cylinder | sphere | cone |

Match.

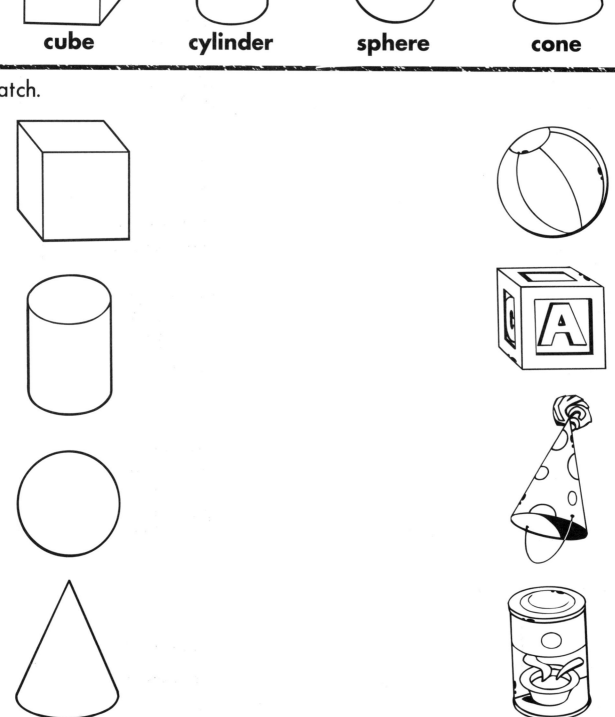

Matching three-dimensional shapes

Shaping Up

Color the circle.

Color the rectangle.

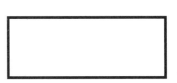

Continue the pattern.

Color the sphere.

Color the cylinder.

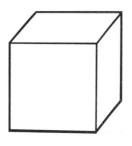

Color the cube.

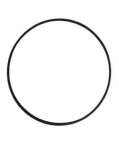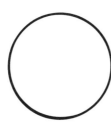

Color the cone.

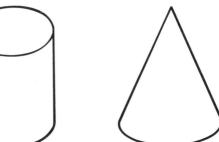

Math Concepts

How Long?

You can use s to measure.
This pencil is 4 ⌐☐s long.

Use real ☐s to measure each picture.
Write the numbers to show how long they are.

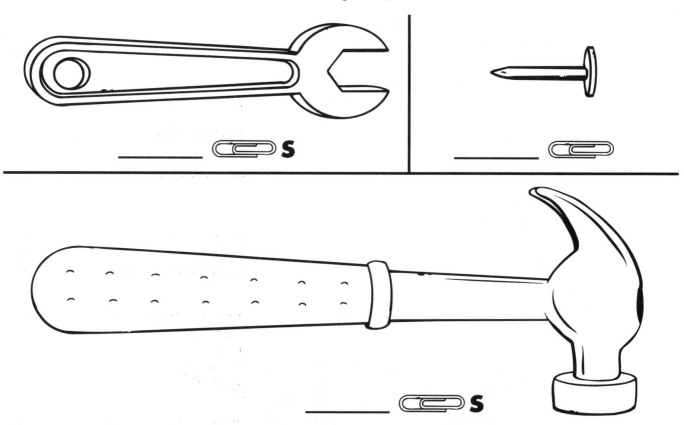

_____ ⌐☐ **S**

_____ ☐

_____ ⌐☐ **S**

Find these objects in your home. Use real ⌐☐s to measure them.
Then write how long they are.

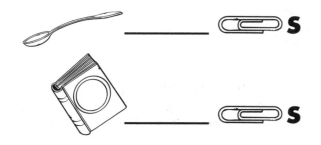 _____ ⌐☐ **S**

_____ ⌐☐ **S**

 _____ ⌐☐ **S**

 _____ ⌐☐ **S**

Measuring length with nonstandard units

Inching Along

5 inches

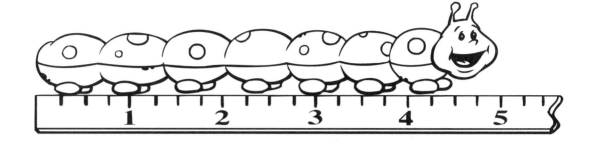

Write the number of inches.

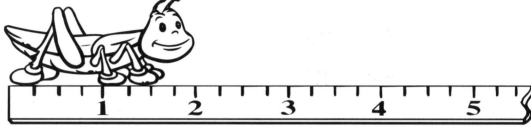

2 _____ inches long

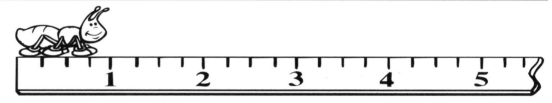

_____ inch long

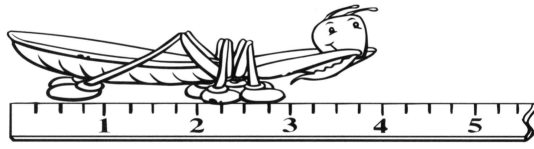

_____ inches long

_____ inches long

Inch by Inch

Measure each worm to the nearest inch. Write about how many inches.

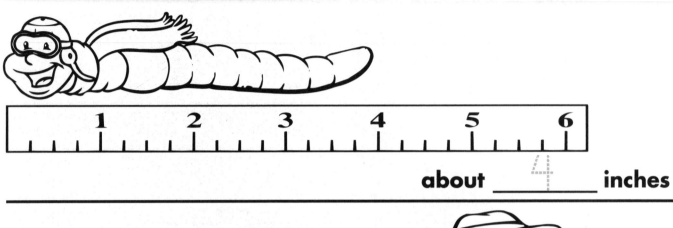

	1	2	3	4	5	6

about _____ inches

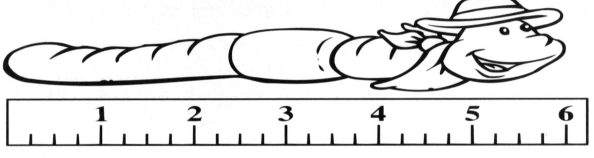

	1	2	3	4	5	6

about _____ inches

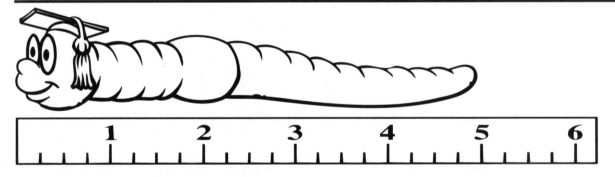

	1	2	3	4	5	6

about _____ inches

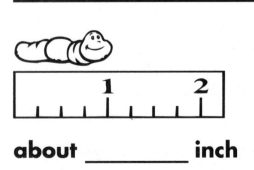

	1	2

about _____ inch

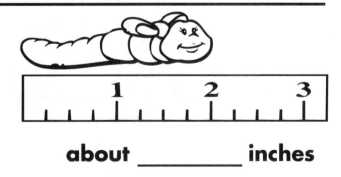

	1	2	3

about _____ inches

Measuring length in inches

Pretty Ribbons

Measure each ribbon to the nearest inch. Write the number.
Color the **longest** ribbon red. Color the **shortest** ribbon blue.

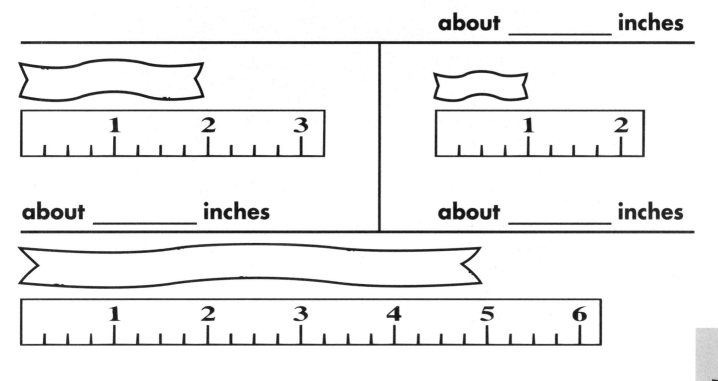

about _____ inches

about _____ inches

about _____ inches

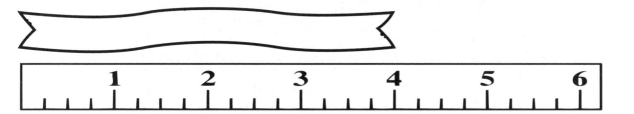

about _____ inches

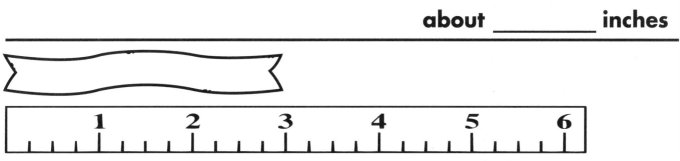

about _____ inches

Math Concepts

Art Fun

Measure each object to the nearest centimeter.
Write about how many centimeters.

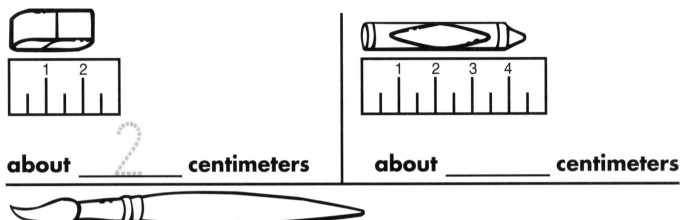

about _____2_____ **centimeters**

about _____ **centimeters**

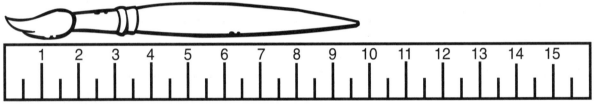

about _____ **centimeters**

about _____ **centimeters**

about _____ **centimeters**

Measuring length in centimeters

Find Sam's Sneaker

Measure each sneaker.
Sam's sneaker is
9 centimeters long.
Find and color it.

| 1 2 3 4 5 |

_____ centimeters

| 1 2 3 4 5 6 7 8 9 10 11 12 13 14 15 |

_____ centimeters

| 1 2 3 4 5 6 7 8 9 10 11 12 13 14 15 |

_____ centimeters

| 1 2 3 4 5 6 7 8 9 10 11 12 13 14 15 |

_____ centimeters

Math Concepts

Measuring length in centimeters

111

Measure at Home

Use a centimeter ruler to measure these things around your home. Write the lengths.

about _____ centimeters

about _____ centimeters

about _____ centimeters

about _____ centimeters

about _____ centimeters

about _____ centimeters

Look for more things to measure. Draw a picture of what you measured and write the length.

What I Measured	Measurement
	about _____ centimeters
	about _____ centimeters
	about _____ centimeters

Measuring length in centimeters

How Much Does It Hold?

less than 1 liter   1 liter   more than 1 liter

Color all the things that hold **more than 1 liter** red.
Color all the things that hold **less than 1 liter** yellow.

Comparing the capacity of containers with 1 liter

Cups, Pints, and Quarts

1 cup

2 cups = 1 pint

4 cups = 1 quart

Color the **cups** to show the same amounts.

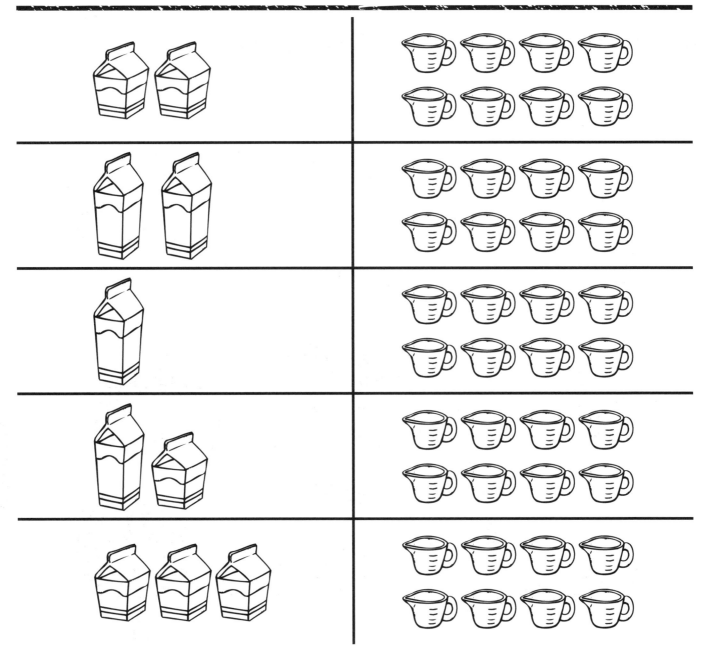

Comparing the capacity of cups, pints, and quarts

Weighing Pounds

This spaghetti weighs 1 **pound**.
Another way to write **pound** is **lb**.

Color the things that weigh **more than** red.

Color the things that weigh **less than** blue.

Math Concepts

Kilograms

**less than
1 kilogram**

**about 1
kilogram**

**more than
1 kilogram**

Another way to write **kilogram** is **kg**.

Color the things that are **less than** green.

Color the things that are **more than** orange.

POTATOES

Comparing weights to 1 kilogram

Review I

Circle the correct answer.

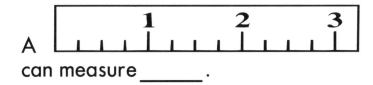

A _____ can measure _____ .

inches   pounds

---

2 s equal _____ .

This  can measure _____ .

kilograms   centimeters

A  weighs _____ .

more than   less than

A  equals _____ .

---

less than   more than

A _____ is _____ .

Review II

Write the length.

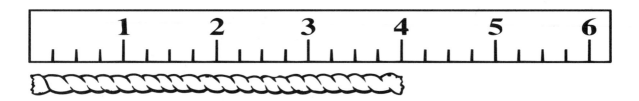

about _____ inches

about _____ centimeters

Color the cups to show the same amount.

Circle the answer that tells about each object's weight.

more than 1 pound

less than 1 pound

more than 1 kilogram

less than 1 kilogram

Reviewing length, capacity, and weight

Equal Parts

2 equal parts   **2 parts not equal**

Color the pictures that show 2 equal parts.

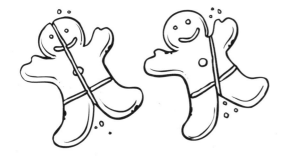

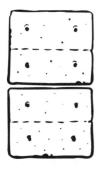 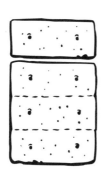

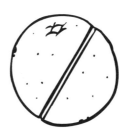 

What is a Half?

1 part shaded
2 equal parts

1/2 or **one half** is shaded.
Two equal parts are **halves**.

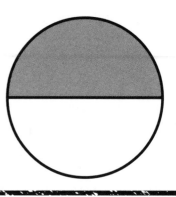

Circle the shapes that show **halves**.
Color **1/2** of each shape you circled.

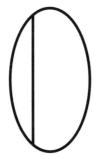

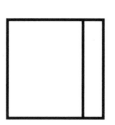

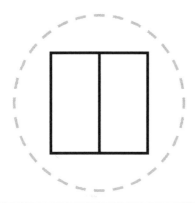

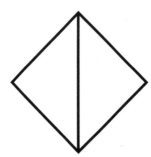

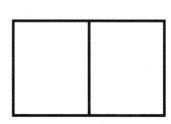

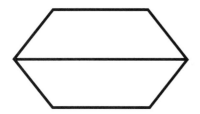

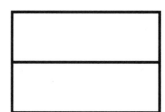

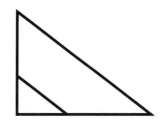

Recognizing halves as two equal parts

What is a Fourth?

1 part shaded
4 equal parts

1/4 or **one quarter** is shaded.
Four equal parts are **fourths**.

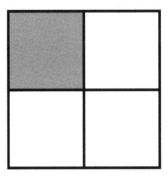

Circle the shapes that show **fourths**.
Color **1/4** of each shape you circled.

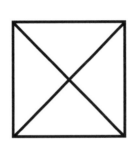
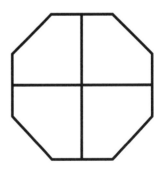

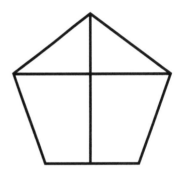

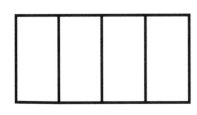
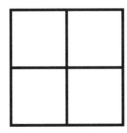
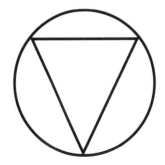

Halves and Fourths

Color **1/2** red.

 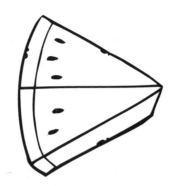 

Color **1/4** orange.

 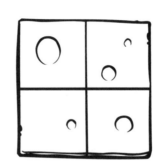 

Color one part. Is it **1/2** or **1/4**? Circle the answer.

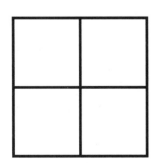 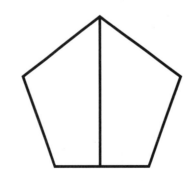 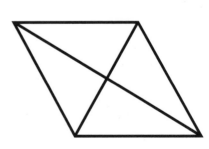

1/2   **1/4**   **1/2**   **1/4**   **1/2**   **1/4**

Recognizing halves and fourths

Answer Key

As the child completes the pages in this section, review his or her answers. When you take the time to correct the work and explain mistakes, you're showing your child that you feel learning is important.

page 98

page 99

page 100

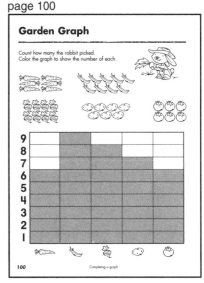

page 101

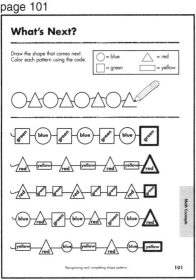

page 102

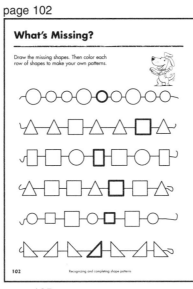

page 103

page 104

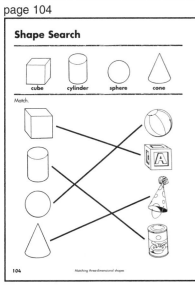

page 105

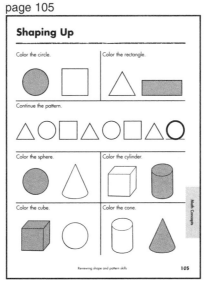

page 106

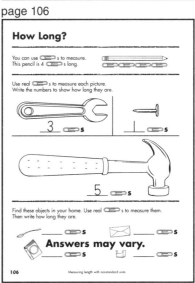

Math Concepts

Inching Along

5 inches

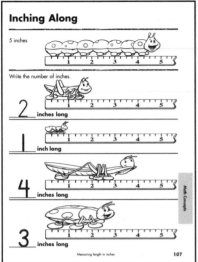

Write the number of inches.

2 inches long

1 inch long

4 inches long

3 inches long

Measuring length in inches   107

Inch by Inch

Measure each worm to the nearest inch. Write about how many inches.

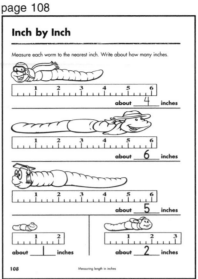

about 4 inches

about 6 inches

about 5 inches

about 1 inches   about 2 inches

108   Measuring length in inches

Pretty Ribbons

Measure each ribbon to the nearest inch. Write the number.
Color the **longest** ribbon red. Color the **shortest** ribbon blue.

about 4 inches

about 2 inches   blue   about 1 inch

red

about 5 inches

about 3 inches

Measuring length in inches   109

Art Fun

Measure each object to the nearest centimeter. Write about how many centimeters.

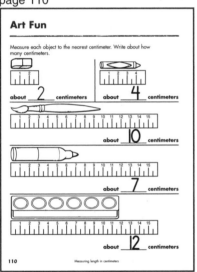

about 2 centimeters   about 4 centimeters

about 10 centimeters

about 7 centimeters

about 12 centimeters

110   Measuring length in centimeters

Find Sam's Sneaker

Measure each sneaker.
Sam's sneaker is
9 centimeters long.
Find and color it.

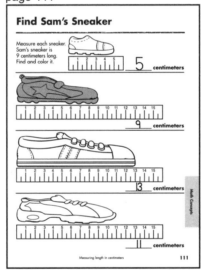

5 centimeters

9 centimeters

13 centimeters

11 centimeters

Measuring length in centimeters   111

Measure at Home

Use a centimeter ruler to measure these things around your home.
Write the lengths.

about _____ centimeters

about _____ centimeters

Answers may vary.   about _____ centimeters

about _____ centimeters

about _____ centimeters

about _____ centimeters

Look for more things to measure. Draw a picture of what you measured and write the length.

What I Measured	Measurement
Answers may vary.	about _____ centimeters
	about _____ centimeters
	about _____ centimeters

112   Measuring length in centimeters

How Much Does It Hold?

less than 1 liter   1 liter   more than 1 liter

Color all the things that hold **more than 1 liter** red.
Color all the things that hold **less than 1 liter** yellow.

yellow   yellow   red

yellow

yellow   red   red

red

Comparing the capacity of containers with 1 liter   113

Cups, Pints, and Quarts

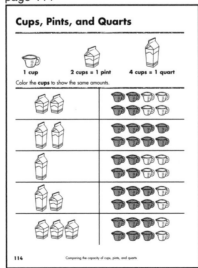

1 cup   2 cups = 1 pint   4 cups = 1 quart

Color the **cups** to show the same amounts.

114   Comparing the capacity of cups, pints, and quarts

Weighing Pounds

This spaghetti weights 1 **pound**.
Another way to write **pound** is **lb**.

Color the things that weigh **more than** red.

Color the things that weigh **less than** blue.

red   red   blue

blue   red   red

blue

blue   blue   red

Comparing weights to 1 pound   115

124   Answers

Kilograms

Review I

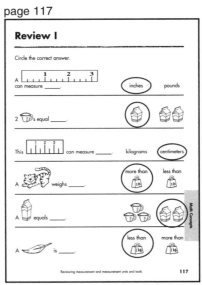

Review II

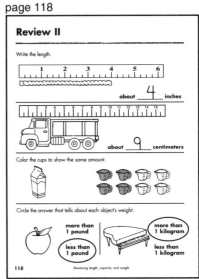

Equal Parts

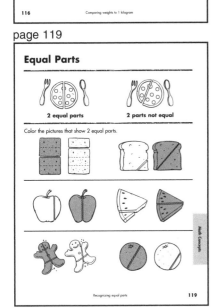

What is a Half?

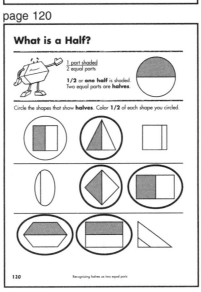

What is a Fourth?

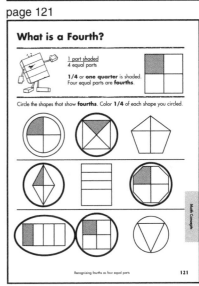

Halves and Fourths

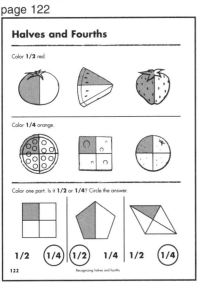

Math Concepts

It's Time

The numbers show the time.
The short hand shows the **hour**.
The long hand shows the **minutes**.
The time is 4 o'clock.

Write the clock numbers.
Color the clock.

Write the numbers.

The hour hand is on _____ .   **It is _____ o'clock.**

The minute hand is on _____ .

Recognizing numerals on a clock and clock parts

What Time Is It?

The **minute hand** is on 12.
The **hour hand** is on 3.
It is 3 o'clock.

Color the hour hand red. Circle the correct time.

5 o'clock

7 o'clock

12 o'clock

1 o'clock

10 o'clock

8 o'clock

11 o'clock

9 o'clock

6 o'clock

7 o'clock

3 o'clock

2 o'clock

Party Time

Draw the hour hand on each clock to show the time.
Color the party hats.

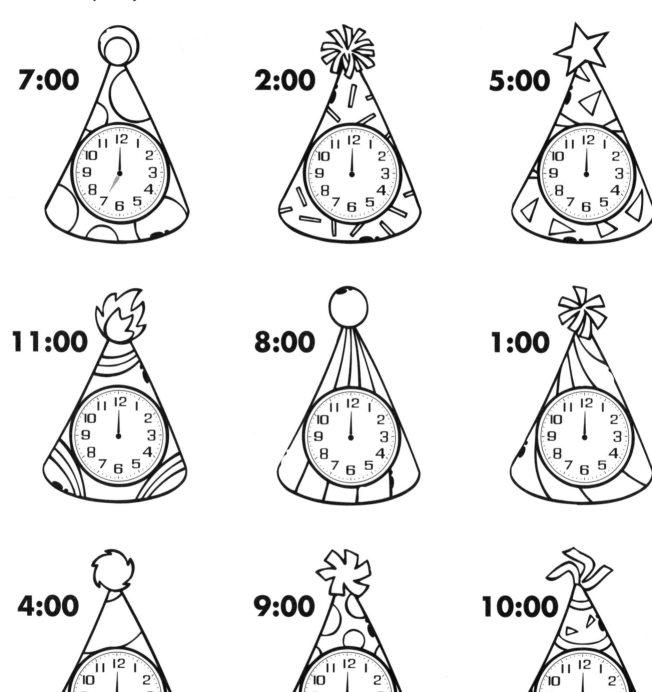

7:00

2:00

5:00

11:00

8:00

1:00

4:00

9:00

10:00

Showing time to the hour on an analog clock

Digital Time

A **digital clock** tells time with just numbers.
First it tells the hour. Then it tells the minutes.

hour → **7:00**

minutes

Write the time on the digital clocks.

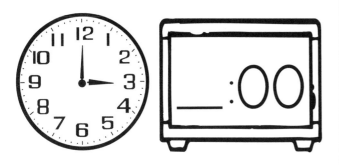

So Many Clocks

4 o'clock

4:00

Draw lines to match the clocks that show the same time.

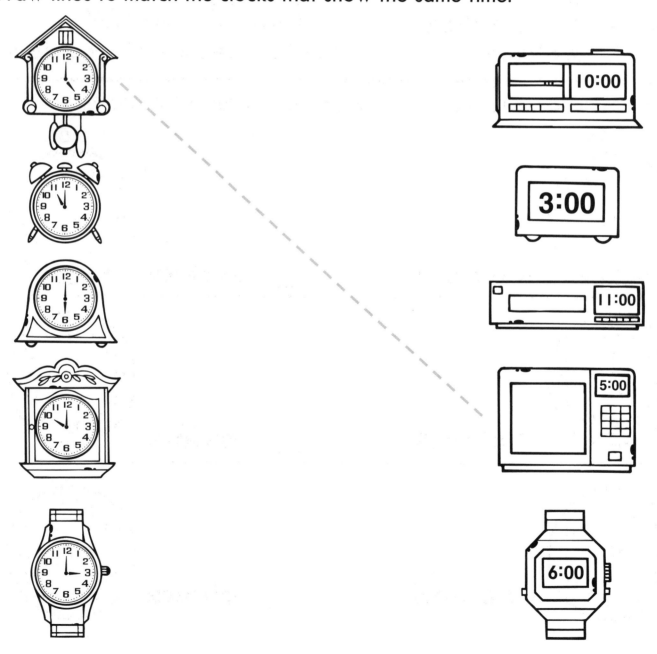

Matching digital and analog clocks showing time to the hour

Now and Later

Now it is **2 o'clock**.

One hour **later** it will be **3 o'clock**.

Draw clock hands to show the time one hour **later**. Write the time.

NOW   **LATER**

4 o'clock   _____ o'clock

7 o'clock   _____ o'clock

10 o'clock   _____ o'clock

Time to the Half Hour

The minute hand is on the 6.
The hour hand is **between** the 8 and 9.
The time is **8:30** or **eight-thirty**.

Circle the correct time.

 9:30

8:30

1:30

11:30

8:30

7:30

5:30

6:30

three-thirty

two-thirty

four-thirty

five-thirty

Telling time to the half hour

Snack Time

The minute hand is on the 6.
The hour hand is **between** 3 and 4.
The time is **3:30** or **three-thirty**.

Draw the hour hand to show the time.
Remember, the hour hand will be **between** two numbers on the clock.

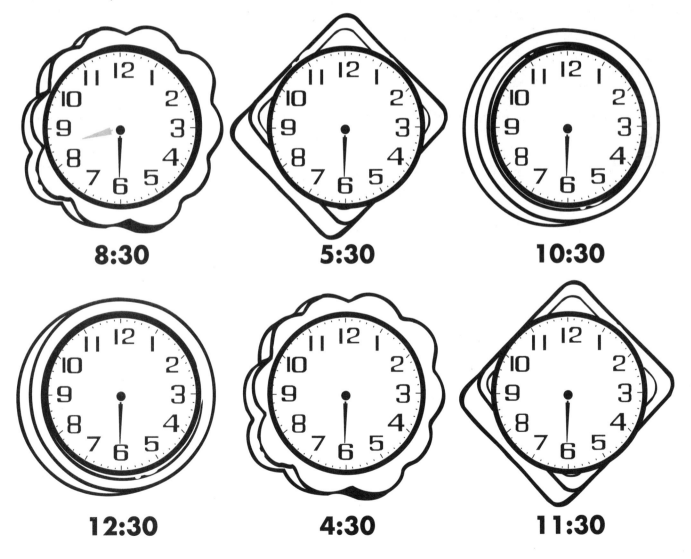

8:30

5:30

10:30

12:30

4:30

11:30

Fishing for Time

Draw a line from each clock to the time it shows.
Then color the clocks and fish using the code.

one-thirty = red	8:30 = green
4:30 = yellow	nine-thirty = blue

8:30

1:30

one-thirty

8:30

4:30

9:30

nine-thirty

4:30

Matching analog and digital clocks to time to the half hour

Time to Clown Around

Write the time.

1:30

Racing Time

Write the time.

7:00

_____

_____

8:30

_____

12:00

_____

_____

_____

5:30

_____

_____

Reading and writing time to the hour and half hour

Penny Pockets

A **penny** is worth **one cent**.
Another way to write **one cent** is **1¢**.

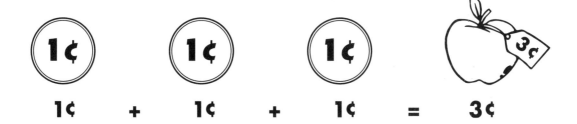

| 1¢ | + | 1¢ | + | 1¢ | = | 3¢ |

Color each penny brown. Write how many. Color the pocket in each row that has more pennies.

_____ pennies

_____ pennies

_____ pennies

_____ pennies

Identifying the value of a penny (one cent piece)

Penny Jars

Draw lines to match the pennies with the amounts.

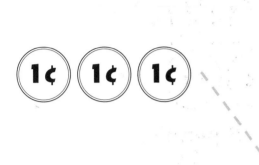

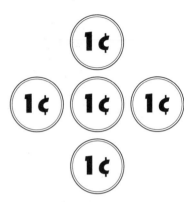

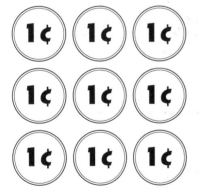

Matching groups of pennies to amounts

Be a Nickel Detective

A **nickel** is worth **five cents** or **5¢**.

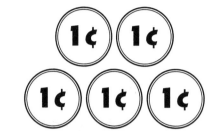

1 nickel
5¢

=

5 pennies
5¢

Color each nickel yellow. Color each penny brown.
Circle the group with the most nickels.

Counting Nickels

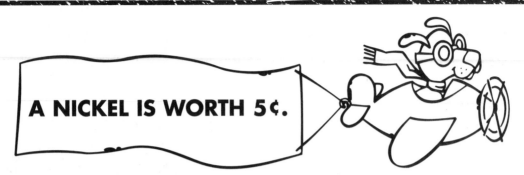

A NICKEL IS WORTH 5¢.

Count by 5's. Write the amount.

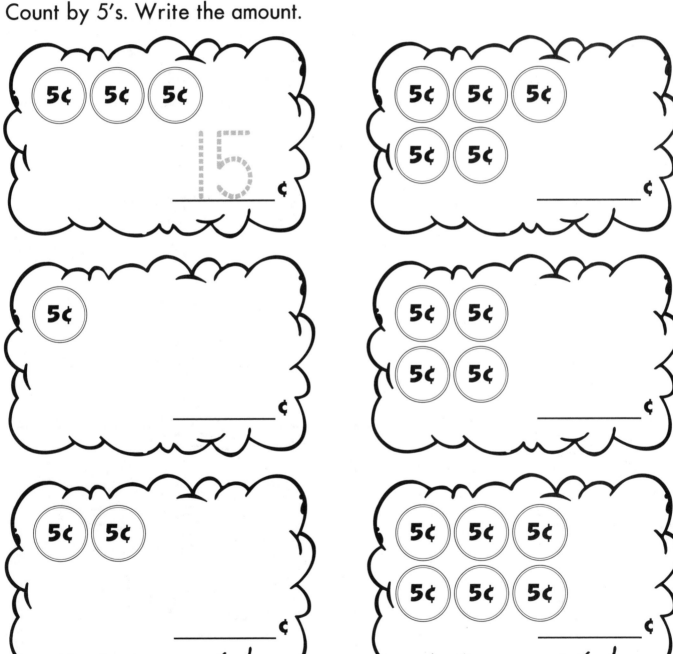

Counting nickels

Coin Count

Count the money in each bank and write the amount. Color the bank with the **most** money pink. Color the one with the **least** money blue.

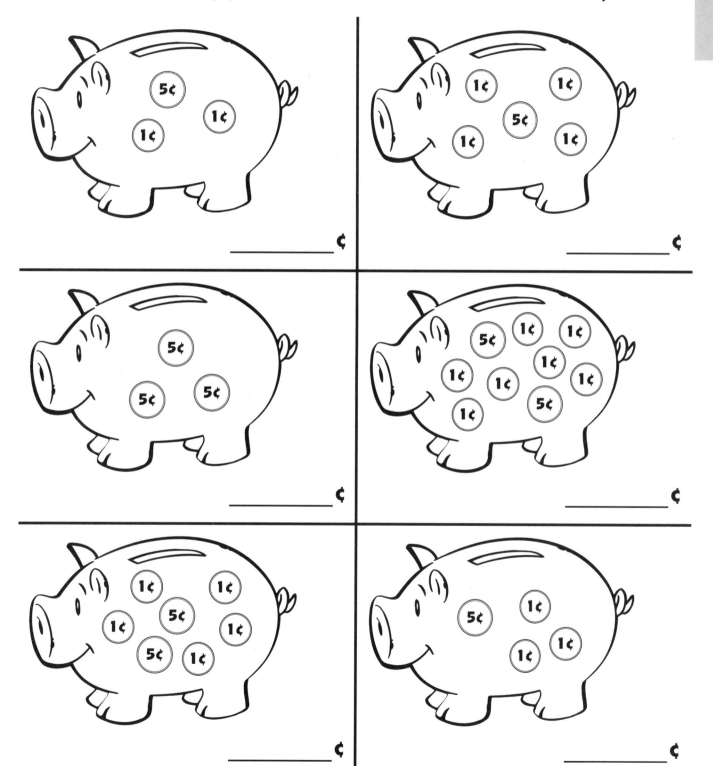

_____ ¢

_____ ¢

_____ ¢

_____ ¢

_____ ¢

_____ ¢

Counting nickels and pennies

A Dime a Glass

A **dime** is worth **ten cents** or **10¢**.

1 dime   =   10 pennies
10¢   10¢

Count the money. Write the amount.

1¢ 1¢ 1¢ 1¢ 1¢ 1¢ 1¢ 1¢ 1¢ 1¢   _____ ¢

10¢   _____ ¢

10¢ 10¢ 1¢   _____ ¢

10¢ 1¢ 1¢ 1¢   _____ ¢

10¢ 1¢ 1¢ 1¢ 1¢ 1¢   _____ ¢

Counting Dimes

Count by 10's. Write the amount.

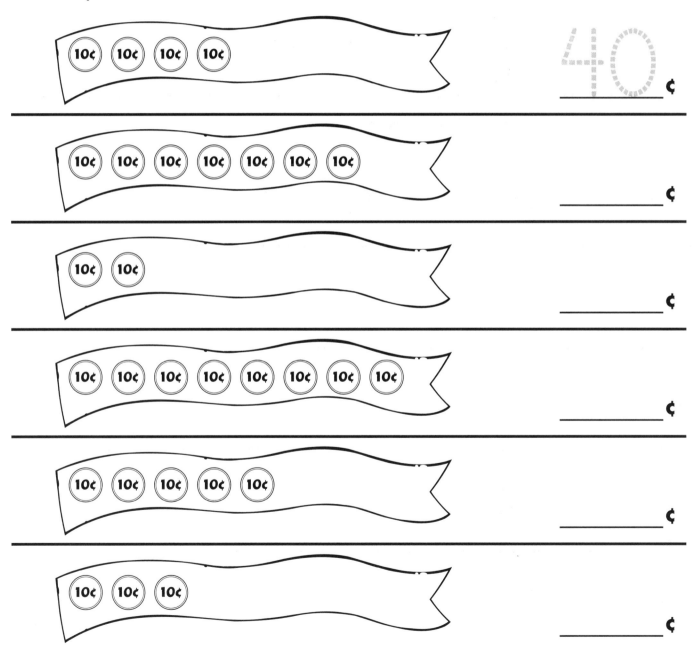

40 ¢

_____ ¢

_____ ¢

_____ ¢

_____ ¢

_____ ¢

Adding Money

Count the money in each group. Add to find the total for the row.

(10¢)   (1¢)(1¢)(1¢)(1¢) (1¢)(1¢)(1¢)

_____ ¢   +   _____ ¢   =   _____ ¢

(10¢)(10¢)   (1¢)(1¢) (1¢)(1¢)

_____ ¢   +   _____ ¢   =   _____ ¢

(10¢)(10¢) (10¢)(10¢)   (1¢)(1¢)

_____ ¢   +   _____ ¢   =   _____ ¢

(10¢)(10¢)(10¢)   (1¢)(1¢)(1¢)

_____ ¢   +   _____ ¢   =   _____ ¢

(10¢)(10¢)(10¢) (10¢)(10¢)   (1¢)

_____ ¢   +   _____ ¢   =   _____ ¢

Counting dimes and pennies

Quarters Anyone?

A **quarter** is worth **twenty-five cents** or **25¢**.

1 quarter	**=**	**2 dimes + 1 nickel**
25¢		**25¢**

Count the money in each purse. Color the purse red if you can trade its coins for a quarter or quarters.

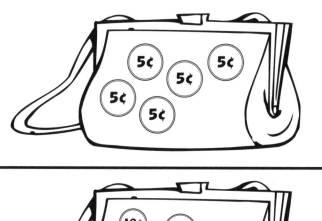

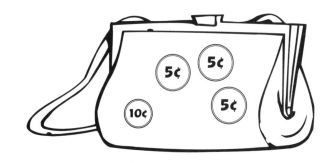

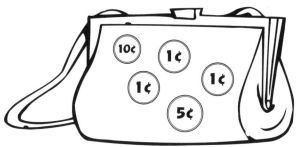

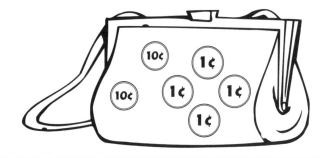

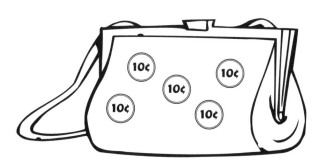

Identifying the value of a quarter (twenty-five cent piece)

145

Coin Collections

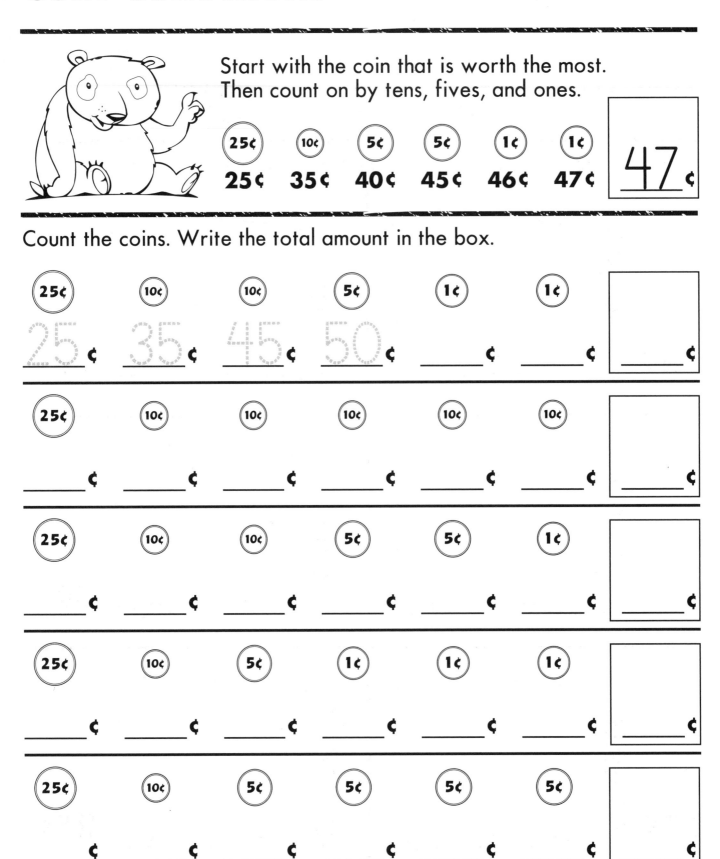

Start with the coin that is worth the most.
Then count on by tens, fives, and ones.

25¢   10¢   5¢   5¢   1¢   1¢

25¢   35¢   40¢   45¢   46¢   47¢

47 ¢

Count the coins. Write the total amount in the box.

25¢   10¢   10¢   5¢   1¢   1¢

25¢   35¢   45¢   50¢   ____¢   ____¢   ____¢

25¢   10¢   10¢   10¢   10¢   10¢

____¢   ____¢   ____¢   ____¢   ____¢   ____¢   ____¢

25¢   10¢   10¢   5¢   5¢   1¢

____¢   ____¢   ____¢   ____¢   ____¢   ____¢   ____¢

25¢   10¢   5¢   1¢   1¢   1¢

____¢   ____¢   ____¢   ____¢   ____¢   ____¢   ____¢

25¢   10¢   5¢   5¢   5¢   5¢

____¢   ____¢   ____¢   ____¢   ____¢   ____¢   ____¢

    Counting quarters, dimes, nickels, and pennies to find money values

Drawing Coins

 1¢   5¢   10¢    25¢

Draw coins to show the amount. You may draw any coins you wish.

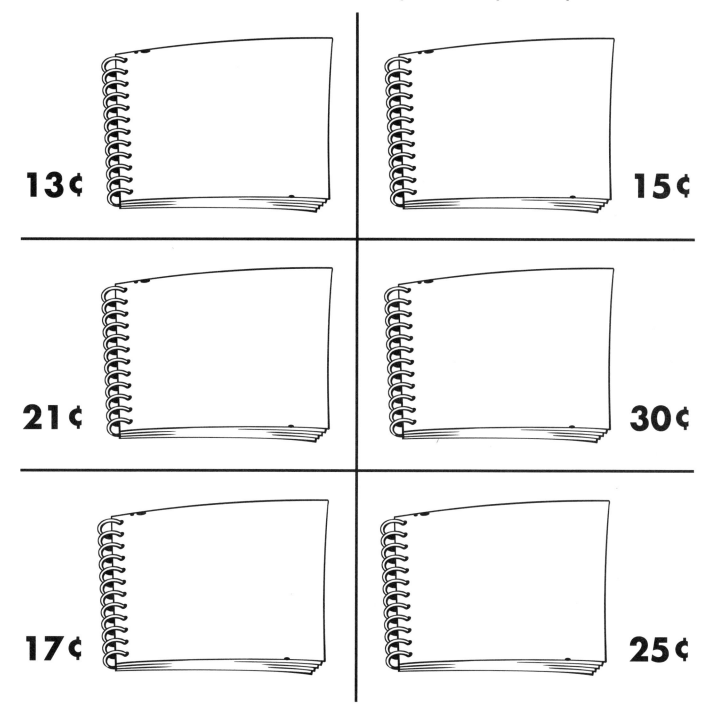

13¢

15¢

21¢

30¢

17¢

25¢

Snack Bar

Read the price of each item. Draw the coins you need to buy it. Then count how many of each coin you drew and write the number.

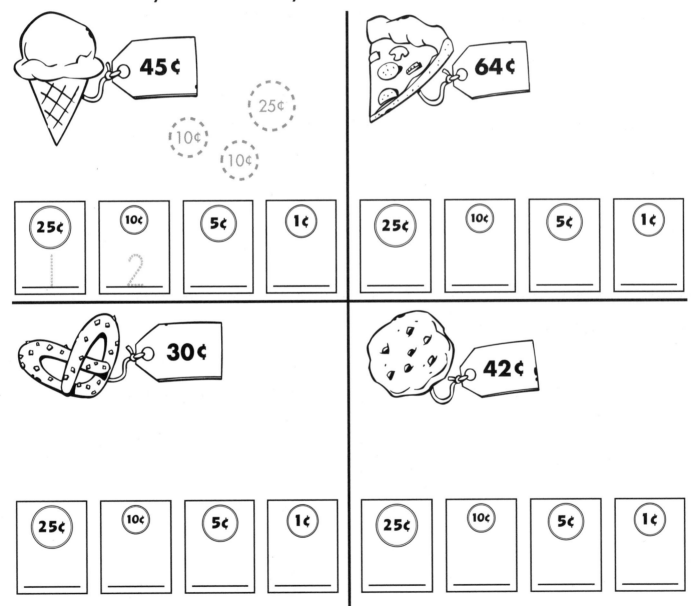

Solving problems using money

Review

Count the money. Write the amount.

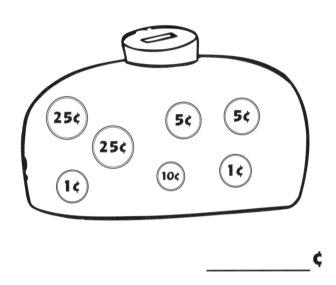

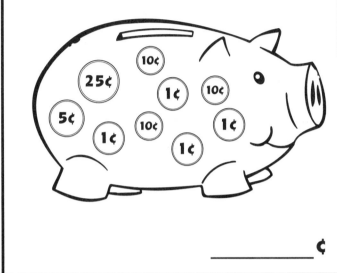

_____ ¢

_____ ¢

Color the coins needed to buy the .

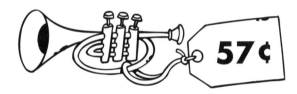

57¢

| 25¢ | 10¢ | 10¢ | 5¢ | 5¢ |

| 5¢ | 1¢ | 1¢ | 1¢ | 1¢ |

Read each problem and circle the answer.

Bob has 1 dime,
2 nickels, and 5 pennies.

Can he trade for a quarter?

Kara has 1 quarter,
and 2 dimes. Lynn has
3 dimes, 2 nickels, and
2 pennies.

Who has more money?

yes   **no**

Kara   **Lynn**

Answer Key

As the child completes the pages in this section, review his or her answers. When you take the time to correct the work and explain mistakes, you're showing your child that you feel learning is important.

page 126

page 127

page 128
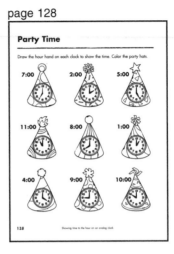

page 129

page 130
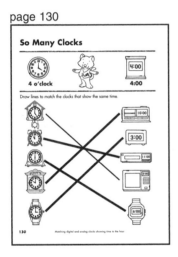

page 131

page 132
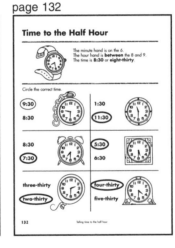

page 133

page 134
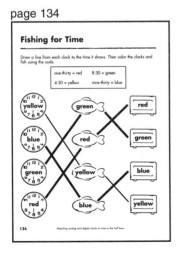

page 135
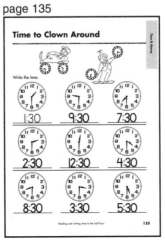

page 136
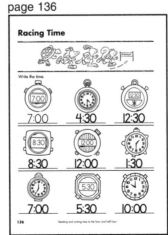

page 137

page 138

Penny Jars

Draw lines to match the pennies with the amounts.

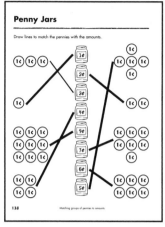

page 139

Be a Nickel Detective

A **nickel** is worth **five cents** or **5¢**.

1 nickel = 5 pennies
5¢   5¢

Color each nickel yellow. Color each penny brown. Circle the group with the most nickels.

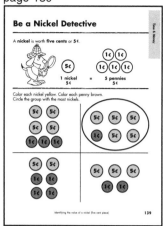

page 140

Counting Nickels

A NICKEL IS WORTH 5¢.

Count by 5's. Write the amount.

15   25
5   20
10   30

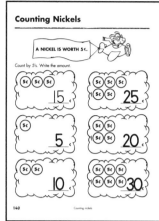

page 141

Coin Count

Count the money in each bank and write the amount. Color the bank with the **most** money pink. Color the one with the **least** money blue.

blue 7   9
15   pink 17
15   8

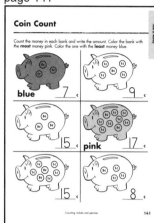

page 142

A Dime a Glass

A **dime** is worth **ten cents** or **10¢**.

1 dime = 10 pennies
10¢   10¢

Count the money. Write the amount.

10¢
10¢
21¢
13¢
15¢

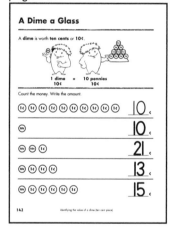

page 143

Counting Dimes

Count by 10's. Write the amount.

40¢
70¢
20¢
80¢
50¢
30¢

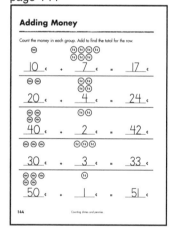

page 144

Adding Money

Count the money in each group. Add to find the total for the row.

10¢ + 7 = 17
20¢ + 4 = 24
40¢ + 2 = 42
30¢ + 3 = 33
50¢ + 1 = 51

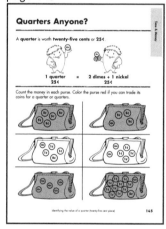

page 145

Quarters Anyone?

A **quarter** is worth **twenty-five cents** or **25¢**.

1 quarter = 2 dimes + 1 nickel
25¢   25¢

Count the money in each purse. Color the purse red if you can trade its coins for a quarter or quarters.

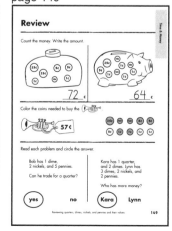

page 146

Coin Collections

Start with the coin that is worth the most. Then count on by tens, fives, and ones.

25¢ 35¢ 40¢ 45¢ 46¢ 47¢   47¢

Count the coins. Write the total amount in the box.

25¢ 35¢ 45¢ 50¢ 51¢ 52¢   52¢
25¢ 35¢ 45¢ 55¢ 65¢ 75¢   75¢
25¢ 35¢ 45¢ 50¢ 55¢ 56¢   56¢
25¢ 35¢ 40¢ 41¢ 42¢ 43¢   43¢
25¢ 35¢ 40¢ 45¢ 50¢ 55¢   55¢

page 147

Drawing Coins

1¢ 5¢ 10¢ 25¢

Draw coins to show the amount. You may draw any coins you wish.

Answers may vary. 13¢
Answers may vary. 15¢
Answers may vary. 21¢
Answers may vary. 30¢
Answers may vary. 17¢
Answers may vary. 25¢

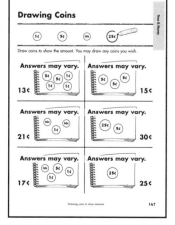

page 148

Snack Bar

I can use 1 quarter and 1 dime.

Read the price of each item. Draw the coins you need to buy it. Then count how many of each coin you drew and write the number.

45¢ Answers may vary. 64¢
2   2 1 4
30¢ Answers may vary. 42¢
1   1 1 2

page 149

Review

Count the money. Write the amount.

72¢   64¢

Color the coins needed to buy the 🎺 57¢

Read each problem and circle the answer.

Bob has 1 dime, 2 nickels, and 5 pennies. Can he trade for a quarter?

yes   no

Kara has 1 quarter, and 2 dimes. Lynn has 3 nickels, and 2 pennies. Who has more money?

Kara   Lynn

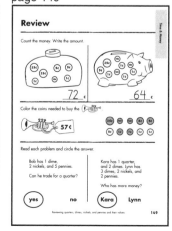

Answers

Lamb in the Sun

Say the name of each picture. Color the lamb and sun. Draw a line from each picture that has the same beginning sound as **lamb** to the lamb. Draw a line from each picture that has the same beginning sound as **sun** to the sun.

Recognizing the initial consonant sounds of **Ll** and **Ss**

Monkeys and Tigers

Say the name of each picture. Color the monkeys and tigers. Draw a line from each picture that has the same beginning sound as **monkey** to the monkeys. Draw a line from each picture that has the same beginning sound as **tiger** to the tigers.

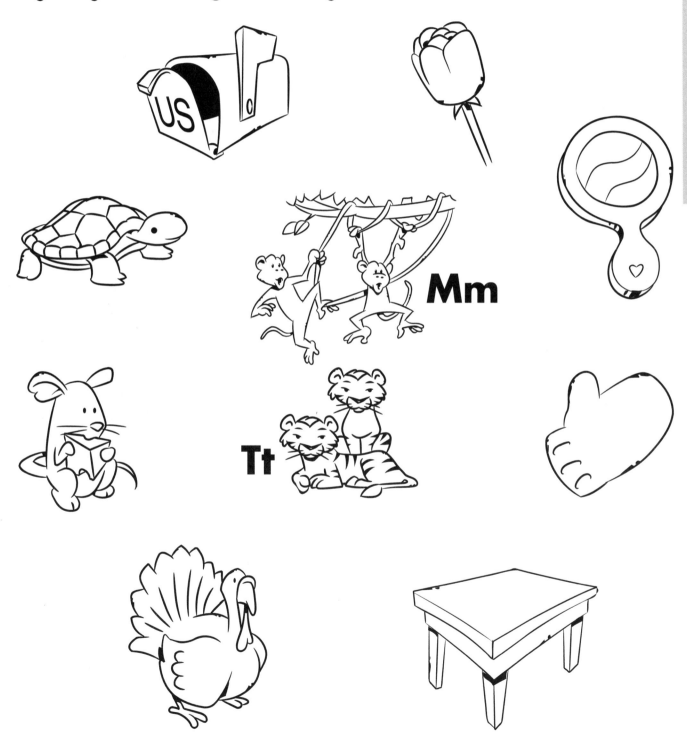

Mm

Tt

Hammer and Nails

Say the name of each picture. Color the hammer and nails. Draw a line from each picture that has the same beginning sound as **hammer** to the hammer. Draw a line from each picture that has the same beginning sound as **nail** to the nails.

Recognizing the initial consonant sounds of **Hh** and **Nn**

Dog Sees a Windmill

Say the name of each picture. Color the dog and windmill. Draw a line from each picture that has the same beginning sound as **dog** to the dog. Draw a line from each picture that has the same beginning sound as **windmill** to the windmill.

Two Sounds of Gg

Hard Sound

When **g** comes before **a**, **o**, or **u**, it has a hard sound like in **gum**.

g<u>oo</u>se   **g<u>a</u>ve**   **g<u>u</u>m**

Soft Sound

When **g** comes before **e**, **i**, or **y**, it often has a soft sound like **j**.

g<u>e</u>neral   **g<u>y</u>psy**
g<u>i</u>ngerbread

The letter **g** does not always have the soft sound before **e** or **i**. Sometimes it has the hard sound, like in **girl**, **get**, and **give**.

Say each word. Circle the **g** and the letter that comes after it. Color the picture if the word has the soft sound of **g**.

giraffe

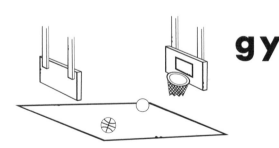
gym

gems
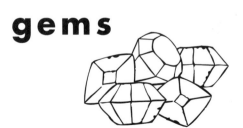

gold

Recognizing the hard and soft consonant sounds of **Gg**

A Rose for Bear

Say the name of each picture. Color the rose and bear. Draw a line from each picture that has the same beginning sound as **rose** to the rose. Draw a line from each picture that has the same beginning sound as **bear** to the bear.

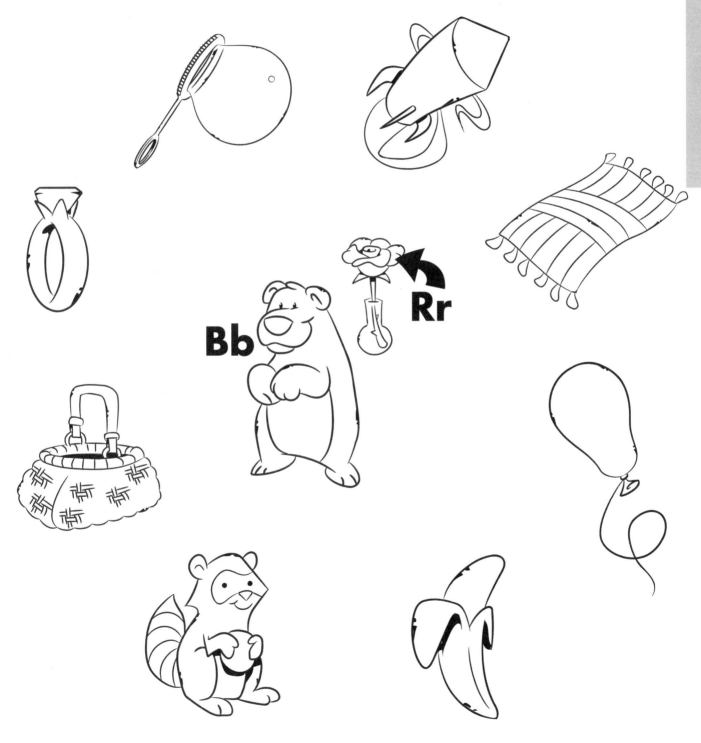

Violin and Yo-Yo

Say the name of each picture. Color the **violin** purple and the **yo-yo** yellow. Color the rest of the pictures using the code.

Same beginning sound as **violin** = purple
Same beginning sound as **yo-yo** = yellow

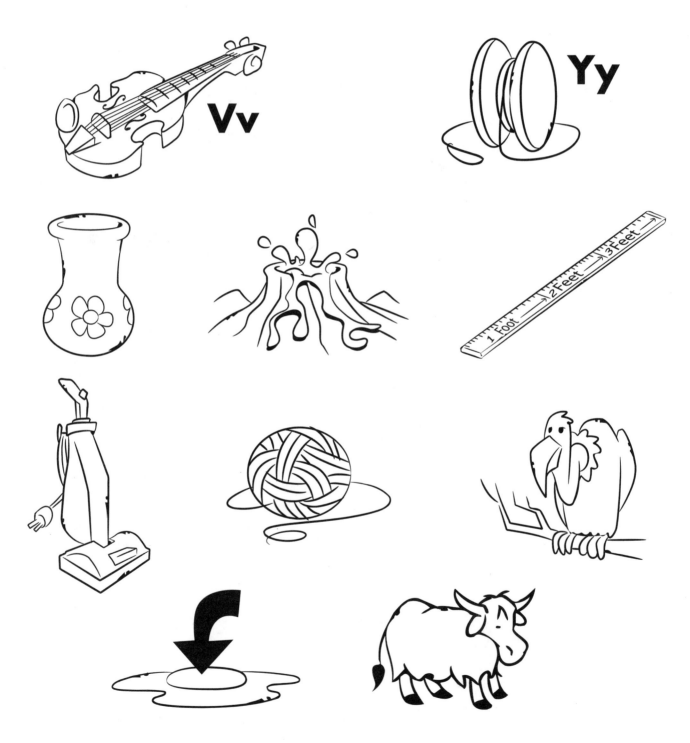

Recognizing the initial consonant sounds of **Vv** and **Yy**

Pandas Around a Fire

Say the name of each picture. Color the **pandas** pink and the **fire** red. Color the rest of the pictures using the code.

Same beginning sound as **panda** = pink
Same beginning sound as **fire** = red

Two Sounds of Cc

Hard Sound

When **c** comes before **a**, **o**, or **u**, it has a hard sound like **k**.

<u>c</u>at   <u>c</u>ub   <u>c</u>ot

Soft Sound

When **c** comes before **e**, **i**, or **y**, it has a soft sound like **s**.

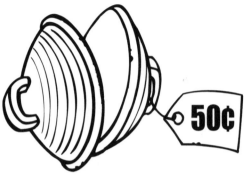

pri<u>c</u>e   <u>c</u>ents
<u>cy</u>mbal

Say each word. Circle the word if it has the hard **c** sound.
Draw a box around the word if it has the soft **c** sound.

celery

car

cup

cone

mice

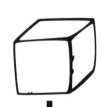

cube

fence

comb

lace

Recognizing the hard and soft consonant sounds of **Cc**

Kettle Juggler

Say the name of each picture. Color the kettles and juggler. Draw a line from each picture that has the same beginning sound as **kettle** to the kettles. Draw a line from each picture that has the same beginning sound as **juggler** to the juggler.

Kk

Jj

Queen and Zebra

Say the name of each picture. Color the queen and zebra. Draw a line from each picture that has the same beginning sound as **queen** to the queen. Draw a line from each picture that has the same beginning sound as **zebra** to the zebra.

Recognizing the initial consonant sounds of **Qq** and **Zz**

Two Sounds of Xx

Say the name of each picture.
Listen for the sound at the end of each word.

six   fo**x**

The letter **x** makes another sound sometimes. When it is at the beginning of a word, **x** often makes the same sound as **z**.

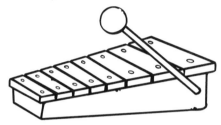 **x**ylophone

Say the name of each picture. Draw a line to the word that names it, then color the picture.

box

ox

ax

tux

What's Missing?

Circle the missing letter in each word, then write it to finish the word. Color the pictures.

h m t	c p s	b f s
___en	___up	___ox
b c h	b c m	f m x
___at	___oat	si___
m p s	b f m	b d p
___ail	___eet	___ig

Reviewing consonant sounds

Hearing Endings

Say the name of each picture, then fill in the circle next to the word that names it. Color the pictures.

○ **map**   ○ **man**   ○ **bun**   ○ **bud**   ○ **fan**   ○ **fat**

○ **bell**   ○ **bet**   ○ **ham**   ○ **hat**   ○ **miss**   ○ **mitt**

○ **win**   ○ **wig**   ○ **cub**   ○ **cup**   ○ **cot**   ○ **cob**

○ **hen**   ○ **hem**   ○ **bob**   ○ **box**   ○ **wet**   ○ **web**

Recognizing the sounds of consonants in final position

Consonant Blends with l

Some **consonants** can be put together to make a **blend**.

The **blend *bl*** has the sound you hear in the word **<u>bl</u>ue**.
The **blend *pl*** has the sound you hear in the word **<u>pl</u>anes**.
The **blend *fl*** has the sound you hear in the word **<u>fl</u>y**.

Color the planes blue. Then read the sentence.

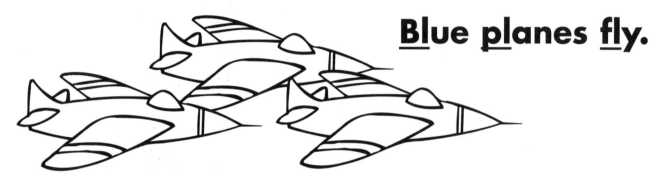

<u>Bl</u>ue <u>pl</u>anes <u>fl</u>y.

Circle the **blends** at the beginning of each word.

clock

slide

glove

black

Write another word that has a consonant blend with the letter **l**.

_____

_ _ _ _ _ _ _ _ _ _ _ _ _ _

_____

Recognizing and writing two-letter initial consonant blends with **l**

Consonant Blends with r

The **blend *dr*** has the sound you hear in the word **<u>dr</u>ew**.

The **blend *gr*** has the sound you hear in the word **<u>gr</u>een**.

The **blend *tr*** has the sound you hear in the word **<u>tr</u>ee**.

Color the tree green. Then read the sentence.

He **<u>dr</u>ew** a **<u>gr</u>een** **<u>tr</u>ee**.

Use the words in the box to write the name of each picture. Notice the **blend** at the beginning of each word.

bricks	dragon	crown	grass

_____   _____

- - - - - - - - - - - - - -   - - - - - - - - - - - - - -

_____   _____

_____   _____

- - - - - - - - - - - - - -   - - - - - - - - - - - - - -

_____   _____

Write another word that has a consonant blend with the letter **r**.

_____

- - - - - - - - - - - - -

_____

Consonant Blends with s

The **blend** *sp* has the sound you hear in the word **sp**ider.
The **blend** *st* has the sound you hear in the word **st**ory.
The **blend** *sc* has the sound you hear in the word **sc**ary.

Read the sentence.

This **sp**ider **st**ory is **sc**ary!

Use the words in the box to write the name of each picture. Notice the **blend** at the beginning of each word.

smile	snail	skate	sweater

Write another word that has a consonant blend with the letter **s**.

Recognizing and writing two-letter initial consonant blends with **s**

Blend or Brend?

Circle each word that begins with the wrong **blend**. Rewrite it using the correct **blend**.

praying catch

_____

- - - - - - - - - - - - - - -

_____

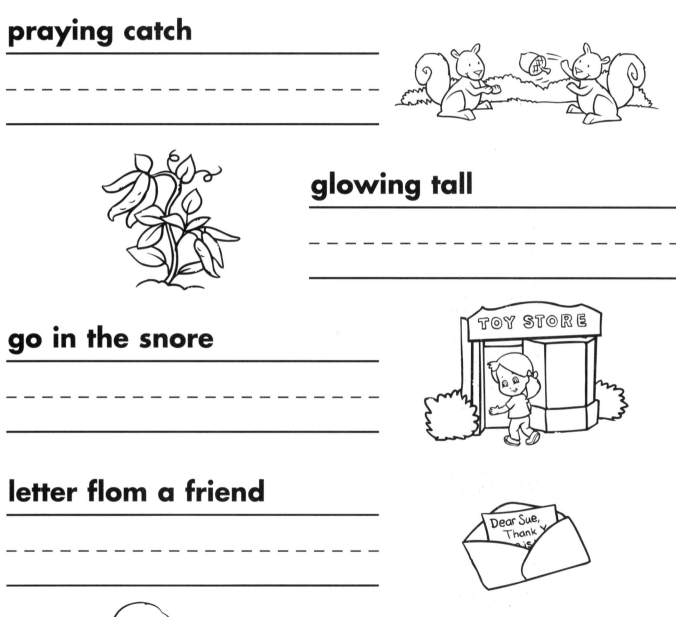

glowing tall

- - - - - - - - - - - - - - -

_____

go in the snore

_____

- - - - - - - - - - - - - - -

_____

letter flom a friend

_____

- - - - - - - - - - - - - - -

_____

pet stider

_____

- - - - - - - - - - - - - - -

_____

Blend at the End

A word may begin or end with a **blend**.

skate     mask

Circle the two-consonant **blend** at the end of each word.

ant	**must**	**felt**
band	**lamp**	**ink**
ask	**lift**	**last**

Write four of the ending **blends** you circled.

_____ _____ _____ _____

Use the words above to write the name of each picture.

 _____

_____

Recognizing two-consonant blends in final position

S and Two Partners

Some **blends** join **s** with *two* other consonants.

He has **<u>str</u>ing**, a **<u>spr</u>ing**, and a **<u>scr</u>ew**.

Use the words in the box to write the name of each picture.
Notice the three-consonant **blend** at the beginning of each word.

spray	scrub	strong	straw

_____

- - - - - - - - - - - - - -

_____

_____

- - - - - - - - - - - - - -

_____

_____

- - - - - - - - - - - - - -

_____

_____

- - - - - - - - - - - - - -

_____

*Recognizing and writing three-consonant blends with **s***

Where's the Blend?

Look at the words on the apples. If you see a **blend** at the beginning of the word, color the apple red. If you see a **blend** at the end of the word, color the apple yellow. Then color the rest of the picture.

Reviewing consonant blends: initial and in final position

Apple Has Short a

_a_pple   b_a_t

Say the name of each picture. If you hear the short **a** sound, write **a** to finish the word.

c__t	f__n	m____n	____x
g____m	p____d	s____ck	s____ck
s____nd	p____g	h____m	d____g
p____t	t____g	p____n	p____n

Recognizing the short **a** sound; completing words with short **a**   **173**

Meet Some Short a Families

tag ____ bag

Read the rhyming words in the first box in each row and circle the ending they share. Use the picture clue to write one more rhyming word.

		ending		
bad	mad	ab		
dad	pad	**ad**		
had	lad	ag		
pan	ran	ad		
tan	man	**an**		
fan	van	ax		
pat	rat	**at**		
fat	mat	ar		
sat	cat	ag		
lap	rap	ab		
tap	gap	at		
nap	cap	**ap**		

Egg Has Short e

_e_gg     b_e_ll

Say the name of each picture. If you hear the short **e** sound, write **e** to finish the word.

b___d	l___g	c___p	h___nd
b___lt	fr___g	tw___lve	n___t
p___n	n___st	f___t	p___t
d___sh	m___n	j___t	r___f

Meet Some Short e Families

Read the rhyming words in the first box in each row and circle the ending they share. Use the picture clue to write one more rhyming word.

		ending		
bet	pet	**el** **et** **ed**		_____
met	wet			- - - - - - - - -
set	let			_____
fell	tell	**ess** **ell**		_____
bell	sell			- - - - - - - - -
				_____
red	fed	**et** **ed**		_____
led	wed			- - - - - - - - -
				_____
ten	den	**en** **et**		_____
pen	men			- - - - - - - - -
				_____
best	pest	**est** **elt** **ent**		_____
rest	west			- - - - - - - - -
test	vest			_____

Recognizing word families with short e

Hill Has Short i

 h<u>i</u>ll

 d<u>i</u>g

Say the name of each picture. If you hear the short **i** sound, write **i** to finish the word.

p___n	h__t	k___ng	b__t
b___gs	k___ck	b__t	m___tt
l___ps	ch___n	l___ck	l___ck
f__n	f__n	w___g	w___ll

Meet Some Short i Families

Read the rhyming words in the first box in each row and circle the ending they share. Use the picture clue to write one more rhyming word.

big dig fig jig rig wig	ending it in ig	_____ - - - - - - - - - - - _____
lip zip sip dip tip rip	ending in ir ip	_____ - - - - - - - - - - - _____
hid bid kid rid	ending ip id	_____ - - - - - - - - - - - _____
lit hit fit bit quit kit	ending is it ig	_____ - - - - - - - - - - - _____
fin tin kin win	ending it in	_____ - - - - - - - - - - - _____

Recognizing word families with short **i**

Ox Has Short o

ox 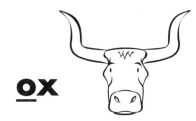    sock

Say the name of each picture. If you hear the short **o** sound, write **o** to finish the word.

Phonics I

p___g	b___x	m___p	h___ll
cl___ck	s___d	s___b	d___ck
p___p	b___g	c___t	c___t
p___p	d___sk	d___ll	r___ck

Recognizing the sound of short **o**; completing words with short **o**   179

Meet Some Short o Families

Read the rhyming words in the first box in each row and circle the ending they share. Use the picture clue to write one more rhyming word.

		ending		
bob	mob	**ob**		_____
job	rob	**op**		_ _ _ _ _ _ _ _
		ending		
hop	mop	**od**		_____
pop	sop	**op**		_ _ _ _ _ _ _ _
		ending		
lot	got	**on**		_____
rot	not	**og**		_ _ _ _ _ _ _ _
pot	hot	**ot**		
		ending		
dock	sock	**ock**		_____
flock	rock	**ogs**		_ _ _ _ _ _ _ _
		ending		
dog	jog	**og**		_____
fog	hog	**op**		_ _ _ _ _ _ _ _

Up Has Short u

u̲p   b̲u̲g

Say the name of each picture. If you hear the short **u** sound, write **u** to finish the word.

gl___ss	d___ck	c___b	c___b
r___t	r___g	c___p	c___p
j___t	g___m	c___t	c___t
s___b	f___t	th___mb	c___ff

Recognizing the sound of short **u**; completing words with short **u**

181

Meet Some Short u Families

Read the rhyming words in the first box in each row and circle the ending they share. Use the picture clue to write one more rhyming word.

	ending		
rug tug hug dug bug mug	**ub** **ug** **up**		_____
cub sub rub hub	**ub** **ud**		_____
fun run bun pun	**un** **ug**		_____
sum bum hum	**um** **un**		_____
hut but cut	**ut** **ud**		_____

Recognizing word families with short **u**

Short Vowel Art

Read the word in each space and listen for the vowel sound. Then color the spaces using the code to show the vowels being used in the words.

short **a** = orange	short **i** = red	short **u** = green
short **e** = blue	short **o** = purple	☆ = yellow

Reviewing the short sounds of the vowels **a, e, i, o,** and **u**

Answer Key

As the child completes the pages in this section, review his or her answers. When you take the time to correct the work and explain mistakes, you're showing your child that you feel learning is important.

page 152

Lamb in the Sun

Say the name of each picture. Color the lamb and sun. Draw a line from each picture that has the same beginning sound as **lamb** to the lamb. Draw a line from each picture that has the same beginning sound as **sun** to the sun.

page 153

Monkeys and Tigers

Say the name of each picture. Color the monkeys and tigers. Draw a line from each picture that has the same beginning sound as **monkey** to the monkeys. Draw a line from each picture that has the same beginning sound as **tiger** to the tigers.

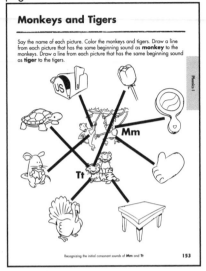

page 154

Hammer and Nails

Say the name of each picture. Color the hammer and nails. Draw a line from each picture that has the same beginning sound as **hammer** to the hammer. Draw a line from each picture that has the same beginning sound as **nail** to the nails.

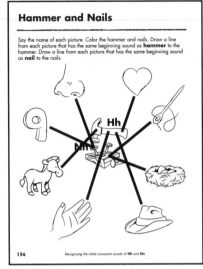

page 155

Dog Sees a Windmill

Say the name of each picture. Color the dog and windmill. Draw a line from each picture that has the same beginning sound as **dog** to the dog. Draw a line from each picture that has the same beginning sound as **windmill** to the windmill.

page 156

Two Sounds of Gg

Hard Sound
When **g** comes before **a**, **o**, or **u**, it has a hard sound like in **gum**.

Soft Sound
When **g** comes before **e**, **i**, or **y**, it often has a soft sound like **J**.

goose   gave   gum

general   gypsy
gingerbread

The letter **g** does not always have the soft sound before **e** or **i**. Sometimes it has the hard sound, like in **girl**, **get**, and **give**.

Say each word. Circle the **g** and the letter that comes after it. Color the picture if the word has the soft sound of **g**.

page 157

A Rose for Bear

Say the name of each picture. Color the rose and bear. Draw a line from each picture that has the same beginning sound as **rose** to the rose. Draw a line from each picture that has the same beginning sound as **bear** to the bear.

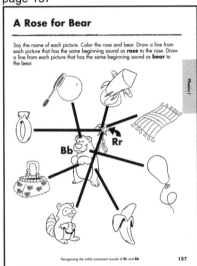

page 158

Violin and Yo-Yo

Say the name of each picture. Color the **violin** purple and the **yo-yo** yellow. Color the rest of the pictures using the code.

Same beginning sound as **violin** = purple
Same beginning sound as **yo-yo** = yellow

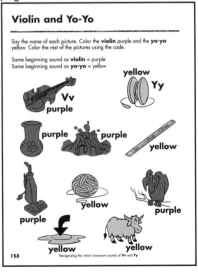

page 159

Pandas Around a Fire

Say the name of each picture. Color the **pandas** pink and the **fire** red. Color the rest of the pictures using the code.

Same beginning sound as **panda** = pink
Same beginning sound as **fire** = red

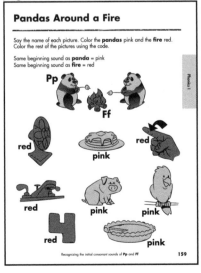

page 160

Two Sounds of Cc

Hard Sound
When **c** comes before **a**, **o**, or **u**, it has a hard sound like **k**.

Soft Sound
When **c** comes before **e**, **i**, or **y**, it has a soft sound like **s**.

cat   cub   cot

price   cents
cymbal

Say each word. Circle the word if it has the hard **c** sound. Draw a box around the word if it has the soft **c** sound.

page 161

Kettle Juggler

Say the name of each picture. Color the kettles and juggler. Draw a line from each picture that has the same beginning sound as **kettle** to the kettles. Draw a line from each picture that has the same beginning sound as **juggler** to the juggler.

Kk

Jj

Recognizing the initial consonant sounds of Kk and Jj   161

page 162

Queen and Zebra

Say the name of each picture. Color the queen and zebra. Draw a line from each picture that has the same beginning sound as **queen** to the queen. Draw a line from each picture that has the same beginning sound as **zebra** to the zebra.

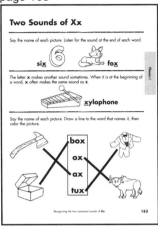

Qq   Zz

162   Recognizing the initial consonant sounds of Qq and Zz

page 163

Two Sounds of Xx

Say the name of each picture. Listen for the sound at the end of each word.

six **6**   fox

The letter **x** makes another sound sometimes. When it is at the beginning of a word, **x** often makes the same sound as **z**.

<u>x</u>ylophone

Say the name of each picture. Draw a line to the word that names it, then color the picture.

box
ox
ax
tux

Recognizing the two consonant sounds of Xx   163

page 164

What's Missing?

Circle the missing letter in each word, then write it to finish the word. Color the pictures.

(h) t	(c) s	(f) s
h e n	c u p	f o x
b (h)	(c) c	f (x) m
h a t	c o a t	s i x
(p) m	(f) m	b (p) d
p a i l	f e e t	p i g

164   Reviewing consonant sounds

page 165

Hearing Endings

Say the name of each picture, then fill in the circle next to the word that names it. Color the pictures.

●map ○man	●bun ●bud	●fan ○fat
●bell ○bet	●ham ○hat	○miss ●mitt
○win ●wig	●cub ○cup	●cot ●cob
●hen ○hem	○bob ●box	○wet ●web

Recognizing the sounds of consonants in final position   165

page 166

Consonant Blends with l

Some **consonants** can be put together to make a **blend**.

The **blend bl** has the sound you hear in the word **blue**.
The **blend pl** has the sound you hear in the word **planes**.
The **blend fl** has the sound you hear in the word **fly**.

Color the planes blue. Then read the sentence.

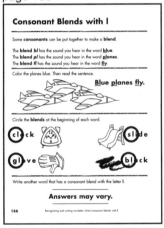

Blue planes fly.

Circle the **blends** at the beginning of each word.

(cl)ock   (sl)ide
(gl)ove   (bl)ack

Write another word that has a consonant blend with the letter **l**.

Answers may vary.

166   Recognizing and writing two-letter initial consonant blends with l

page 167

Consonant Blends with r

The **blend dr** has the sound you hear in the word **drew**.
The **blend gr** has the sound you hear in the word **green**.
The **blend tr** has the sound you hear in the word **tree**.
Color the tree green. Then read the sentence.

He **drew** a **green tree**.

Use the words in the box to write the name of each picture. Notice the **blend** at the beginning of each word.

| bricks | dragon | crown | grass |

crown   grass
bricks   dragon

Write another word that has a consonant blend with the letter **r**.

Answers may vary.

Recognizing and writing two-letter initial consonant blends with r   167

page 168

Consonant Blends with s

The **blend sp** has the sound you hear in the word **spider**.
The **blend st** has the sound you hear in the word **story**.
The **blend sc** has the sound you hear in the word **scary**.
Read the sentence.

This **spider story** is **scary**!

Use the words in the box to write the name of each picture. Notice the **blend** at the beginning of each word.

| smile | snail | skate | sweater |

snail   sweater
smile   skate

Write another word that has a consonant blend with the letter **s**.

Answers may vary.

168   Recognizing and writing two-letter initial consonant blends with s

page 169

Blend or Brend?

Circle each word that begins with the wrong **blend**. Rewrite it using the correct **blend**.

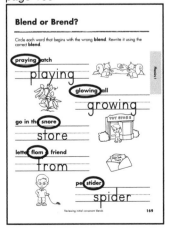

(praying)atch
playing

(glowing)all
growing

go in the (snore)
store

letter (flom) friend
from

pe(stider)
spider

Reviewing initial consonant blends   169

page 170

Blend at the End

A word may begin or end with a **blend**.

skate   **mask**

Circle the two-consonant **blend** at the end of each word.

a(nt)   mu(st)   fe(lt)
ba(nd)   la(mp)   i(nk)
a(sk)   li(ft)   la(st)

Write four of the ending **blends** you circled.

Answers may vary.

Use the words above to write the name of each picture.

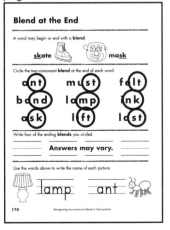

lamp   ant

170   Recognizing two-consonant blends in final position

page 171

S and Two Partners

Some **blends** join **s** with two other consonants.

He has a **string**, a **spring**, and a **screw**.

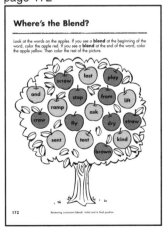

Use the words in the box to write the name of each picture. Notice the three-consonant **blend** at the beginning of each word.

| spray | scrub | strong | straw |

straw   spray
scrub   strong

Recognizing and writing three-consonant blends with s   171

page 172

Where's the Blend?

Look at the words on the apples. If you see a **blend** at the beginning of the word, color the apple red. If you see a **blend** at the end of the word, color the apple yellow. Then color the rest of the picture.

172   Reviewing consonant blends: initial and final position

page 173

Apple Has Short a

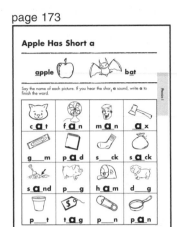

apple   bat

Say the name of each picture. If you hear the short a sound, write a to finish the word.

c**a**t	f**a**n	m**a**n	**a**x
g__m	p**a**d	s__ck	s**a**ck
s**a**nd	p__g	h**a**m	d__g
p__t	t**a**g	p__n	p**a**n

Recognizing the short a sound; completing words with short a   173

page 174

Meet Some Short a Families

tag   bag

Read the rhyming words in the first box in each row and circle the ending they share. Use the picture clue to write one more rhyming word.

		ending	
bad mad		(ad) ab ag	sad
dad pad			
had lad			
pan ran		ad (an) ax	can
tan man			
fan van			
pat rat		(at) an ag	hat
fat mat			
sat cat			
lap rap		ab at (ap)	map
tap gap			
nap cap			

174   Recognizing word families with short a

page 175

Egg Has Short e

egg   bell

Say the name of each picture. If you hear the short e sound, write e to finish the word.

b**e**d	l**e**g	c__p	h__nd
b__lt	fr__g	tw**e**lve	n**e**t
p**e**n	n**e**st	f__t	p**e**t
d__sh	m**e**n	j**e**t	r__f

Recognizing the sound of short e; completing words with short e   175

page 176

Meet Some Short e Families

Read the rhyming words in the first box in each row and circle the ending they share. Use the picture clue to write one more rhyming word.

		ending	
bet pet		(et) ed	net
met wet			
set let			
fell tell		ee (ell)	well
bell sell			
red fed		(ed)	bed
led wed			
ten den		(en) et	hen
pen men			
best pest		(est) ell ent	nest
rest west			
test vest			

176   Recognizing word families with short e

page 177

Hill Has Short i

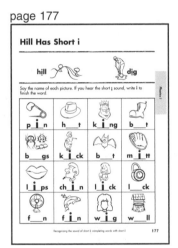

hill   dig

Say the name of each picture. If you hear the short i sound, write i to finish the word.

p**i**n	h__t	k**i**ng	b__t
b__gs	k**i**ck	b__t	m**i**tt
l**i**ps	ch**i**n	l**i**ck	l__ck
f__n	f**i**n	w**i**g	w__ll

Recognizing the sound of short i; completing words with short i   177

page 178

Meet Some Short i Families

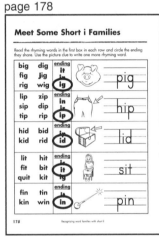

Read the rhyming words in the first box in each row and circle the ending they share. Use the picture clue to write one more rhyming word.

		ending	
big dig		it (ig)	pig
fig jig			
rig wig			
lip zip		in (ip)	hip
sip dip			
tip rip			
hid bid		ig (id)	lid
kid rid			
lit hit		(it) ig	sit
fit bit			
quit kit			
fin tin		(in)	pin
kin win			

178   Recognizing word families with short i

page 179

Ox Has Short o

ox   sock

Say the name of each picture. If you hear the short o sound, write o to finish the word.

p__g	b**o**x	m**o**p	h__ll
cl**o**ck	s__d	s__b	d__ck
p**o**p	b__g	c**o**t	c__t
p__p	d__sk	d**o**ll	r**o**ck

Recognizing the sound of short o; completing words with short o   179

page 180

Meet Some Short o Families

Read the rhyming words in the first box in each row and circle the ending they share. Use the picture clue to write one more rhyming word.

		ending	
bob mob		(ob) op	cob
job rob			
hop mop		(op)	top
pop sop			
lot got		on og (ot)	cot
rot not			
pot hot			
dock sock		(ock) ogs	lock
flock rock			
dog jog		(og)	log
fog hog			

180   Recognizing word families with short o

page 181

Up Has Short u

up   bug

Say the name of each picture. If you hear the short u sound, write u to finish the word.

gl__ss	d**u**ck	c**u**b	c__p
r__t	r**u**g	c__p	c**u**p
j__t	g**u**m	c**u**t	c__t
s**u**b	f__t	th**u**mb	c**u**ff

Recognizing the sound of short u; completing words with short u   181

page 182

Meet Some Short u Families

Read the rhyming words in the first box in each row and circle the ending they share. Use the picture clue to write one more rhyming word.

		ending	
rug tug		ub (ug) up	jug
hug dug			
bug mug			
cub sub		(ub) ud	tub
rub hub			
fun run		(un) ut	sun
bun pun			
sum		(um) un	gum
bum			
hum			
hut		ut ud	nut
but			
cut			

182   Recognizing word families with short u

page 183

Short Vowel Art

Read the word in each space and listen for the vowel sound. Then color the spaces using the code to show the vowels being used in the words.

short a = orange	short i = red	short u = green
short e = blue	short o = purple	☆ = yellow

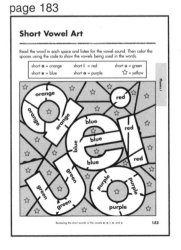

Reviewing the short sounds of the vowels a, e, i, o, and u   183

Silent e and Long Vowels

When a vowel is followed by a single consonant and the letter **e**, it usually takes its long sound. The **e** at the end of the word makes no sound—it's a **silent e**.

a + **c** + **e** = **<u>a</u>c<u>e</u>**

e + **v** + **e** = **<u>e</u>v<u>e</u>**

i + **c** + **e** = **<u>i</u>c<u>e</u>**

bo + **n** + **e** = **b<u>o</u>n<u>e</u>**

flu + **t** + **e** = **fl<u>u</u>t<u>e</u>**

Sound out each word. Draw a circle around the **long vowel** and a square around the **silent e**.

line   **make**   **here**

nose   **cube**

Read the word below. Rewrite it, adding a **silent e** at the end. What new word did you make?

_____ _____

man _____

Silent e Word Play

Say the name of each picture. Fill in the missing vowel and the **silent e** to complete the word.

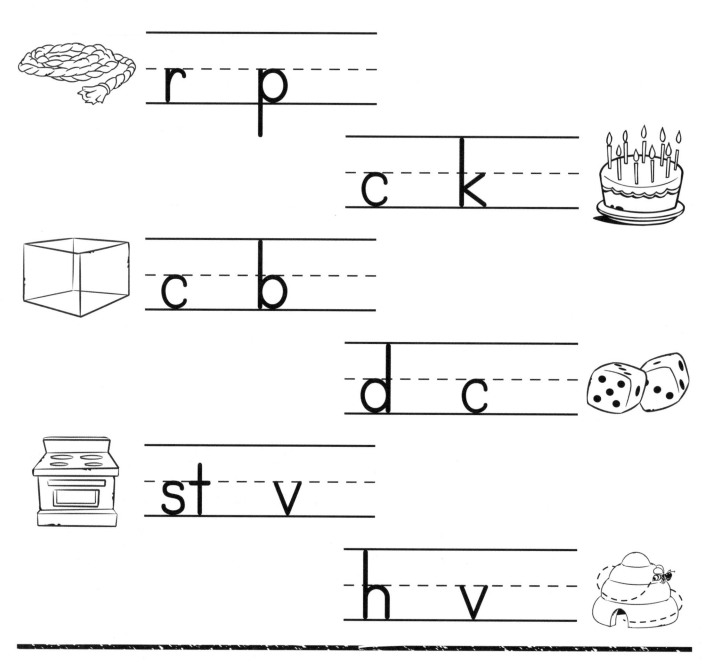

r _ p

c _ k

c _ b

d _ c

st _ v

h _ v

Cross out the **silent e** at the end each word. Sound out the new words that you made.

fine   **huge**   **made**   **note**

Recognizing the effect of **silent e** on vowel sounds

Hearing the Long a Sound

The words **lake** and **train** have the long **a** sound.

lake   **train**

Say the names of the two pictures in each box.
Color the one with the long **a** sound.

Phonics II

Strain Your Brain!

Usually, **ai** has the long **a** sound.

n<u>ai</u>l

 br<u>ai</u>d

Write words from the box to complete each sentence.
Circle **ai** in each word you write.

hail	rain	mail	pail	paint	laid

The _____ is full of

_____ .

Will the _____ bring _____

or _____ ?

I _____ the

_____ on the table.

Recognizing and writing words with long **a** spelled **ai**

Another Way to Make Long a

Usually, **ay** has the long **a** sound.

h<u>ay</u>

 tr<u>ay</u>

Write words from the box to complete each sentence.
Circle **ay** in each word you write.

| clay | pay | day | play | gray | stay |

_____

Every _____ **I**

_____ **with friends.**

I _____ **inside when**

the clouds are _____ **.**

Did you _____

for the _____ **?**

Hearing the Long e Sound

The words **weed** and **meat** have the long **e** sound.

weed   **meat**

Say the names of the two pictures in each box.
Color the one with the long **e** sound.

Identifying the long **e** sound

Neat!

Usually, **ea** has the long **e** sound.

le<u>a</u>f

 s<u>ea</u>l

Write words from the box to complete each sentence.
Circle **ea** in each word you write.

meal	eat	tea	team	leap	cream

_____

We will_____ our

_____ now.

_____

Everyone on the_____

can_____ high.

_____

I put_____

in my_____ .

We Keep Up with e

When the only vowel in a word is one **e** at the end, that **e** usually has a long sound.

be   **he**   **she**   **me**   **we**

Usually, **ee** has the long **e** sound.

kn<u>ee</u> 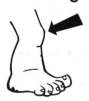    **m<u>ee</u>t**

Circle the word that completes each sentence.

Spring will _____ here soon.

| be | he | me |

Cars drive on the _____.

| sleep | steep | street |

How far can you _____?

| see | seem | sheep |

A _____ is on the flower.

| feet | beef | bee |

I _____ happy today.

| fee | feel | free |

Completing short sentences; recognizing words with long **e** spelled **e** and **ee**

Hearing the Long i Sound

The words **kite** and **light** have the long **i** sound.

kite   **light**

Say the names of the two pictures in each box. Color the one with the long **i** sound.

Like, Lie, Light—All Long i

Usually, **ie** has the long **i** sound.

p<u>ie</u>

 t<u>ie</u>

Usually, **igh** has the long **i** sound.

n<u>igh</u>t

 r<u>igh</u>t

Cross out the word in each box that does not have the long **i** sound.

tie fight ~~fit~~	die did light
lie might fin	night pie pin
tight tin nice	bright tint sigh

Recognizing words with long **i** spelled **ie** and **igh**

Hearing the Long o Sound

The words **nose** and **coat** have the long **o** sound.

nose   coat

Say the names of the two pictures in each box. Color the one with the long **o** sound.

Partners with o

Usually, **oe** at the end of a word has the long **o** sound.

 d<u>oe</u>   **h<u>oe</u>**

Usually, **oa** has the long **o** sound.

c<u>oa</u>st 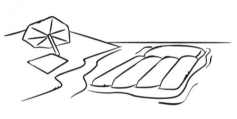 **fl<u>oa</u>t**

Match each word with its picture.

toe

boat

coal

toast

soap

coat

Recognizing words with long **o** spelled **oe** and **oa**

Which Long o Word Fits?

When **o** is at the end of a word, it often takes its long sound.

"H<u>o</u>, h<u>o</u>, h<u>o</u>!"

In many words, **ow** has the long **o** sound.

b<u>ow</u>

 **sn<u>ow</u>**

Circle the long **o** word that best completes each sentence.

We will _____ to the store.

no	go	so

A big, black _____ is on the roof.

row	low	crow

Did the wind _____ the tree down?

mow	blow	throw

I like to sleep in my _____ bed.

own	blown	grown

Hearing the Long u Sound

The words **mule** and **fruit** have the long **u** sound.

mule  **fruit**

Say the names of the two pictures in each box. Color the one with the long **u** sound.

Identifying the long **u** sound

Partners with u

Usually, **ue** has the long **u** sound.

gl<u>ue</u>

 **T<u>ue</u>sday**

In some words, **ui** has the long **u** sound.

fr<u>ui</u>t

 **j<u>ui</u>ce**

Match each word with its picture.

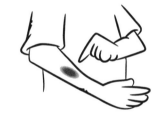

fruit

clue

glue

bruise

cruise

suit

Recognizing words with long **u** spelled **ue** and **ui**

Y as a Vowel

The letter **y** can be used as a vowel as well as a consonant. Sometimes it has the long **i** sound, as in **fly**.

fly

Sometimes it has the long **e** sound, as in **happy**.

happy

Say each word aloud. If it has the long **i** sound, write **i** on the line. If it has the long **e** sound, write **e**. Then color the pictures.

 **cry** _____

 **fry** _____

 **silly** _____

 **family** _____

 **city** _____

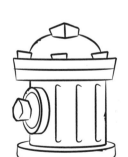 **hydrant** _____

Recognizing the two vowel sounds of **y**: long **i** and long **e**

Are You Ready for ar?

Usually, **ar** has the vowel sound you hear in **b<u>ar</u>n**.

b<u>ar</u>n

Circle the correct name for each picture.

aim **arm**	**pack** **park**	**star** **stay**
make **mark**	**cat** **cart**	**party** **pantry**

Write **ar** to complete each word below. Then read the words aloud.

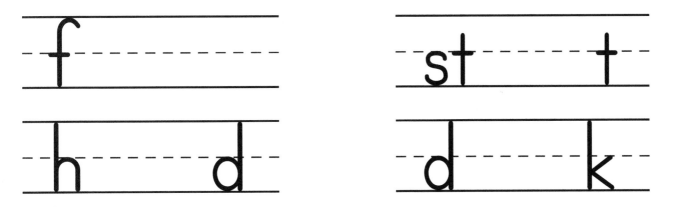

f_____

h_____d

st_____t

d_____k

Don't Forget or!

Usually, **or** has the vowel sound you hear in **fork**.

fork

Circle the correct name for each picture.

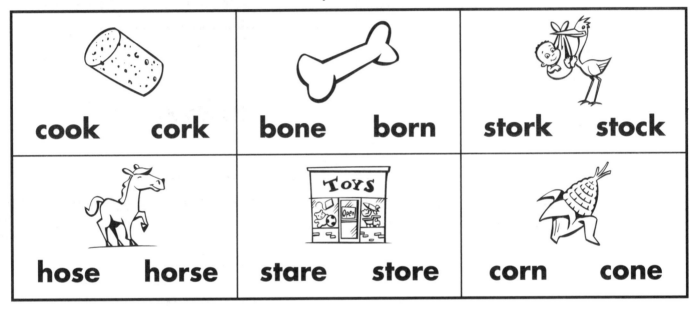

cook **cork**	**bone** **born**	**stork** **stock**
hose **horse**	**stare** **store**	**corn** **cone**

Write **or** to complete each word on the left. Then draw lines to match each **or** word with its opposite.

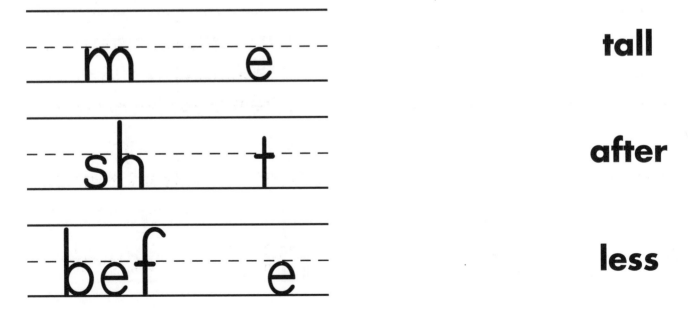

m __ __ e

tall

sh __ __ t

after

bef __ __ e

less

Recognizing the sounds of **r**-controlled vowels

The Early Bird Gets the Worm

The vowel sound is the same in each of the words below.

b<u>ir</u>d **w<u>or</u>m** **t<u>ur</u>n** **f<u>er</u>n** **<u>ear</u>th**

The **ar** in **backw<u>ar</u>d** also has this vowel sound.

backw<u>ar</u>d

Write five different letter pairs that can have the same vowel sound that you hear in **<u>ear</u>th**.

_____   _____

- - - - - - - - -   - - - - - - - - -

_____   _____

_____   _____   _____

- - - - - - -   - - - - - - -   - - - - - - -

_____   _____   _____

Circle the words that have the same vowel sound that you hear in **<u>ear</u>th**.

nurse   **fur**   **four**   **forward**

burn   **more**   **girl**   **word**

Recognizing the sounds of **r**-controlled vowels   **205**

Different Letters, Same Sound

Usually, **aw** has the vowel sound you hear in the word **saw**.

saw

Often, **al** has the same sound.

call    **talk**

Use the words in the box to write the name of each picture.

| salt | walk | ball | yawn | paw | hawk |

_____

- - - - - - - - - -

_____

_____

- - - - - - - - - -

_____

_____

- - - - - - - - - -

_____

_____

- - - - - - - - - -

_____

*Recognizing the vowel sounds of **a**/consonant combinations*

A Moose on the Moon

In some words, **oo** has the vowel sound you hear in **m<u>oo</u>n**.

m<u>oo</u>n

m<u>oo</u>se

f<u>oo</u>d

Match each word with its picture.

boot

goose

noon

roof

tools

tooth

balloon

igloo

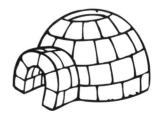

Recognizing the long double **o** sound of **oo**

207

Let's Buy Some New Glue

Often, **ew** and **ue** have the same vowel sound as the **oo** in **moon**.

New Glue on *Sale!*

n<u>**ew**</u>   **gl**<u>**ue**</u>

Choose a word that best completes each sentence and write it on the line.

When will the tulips _____ **?**

| blew | bloom | blue |

Ron _____ **a picture.**

| drew | droop | due |

Mom put meat in the _____ **.**

| clue | gloom | stew |

Anna _____ **the ball.**

| true | threw | troop |

Completing short sentences; recognizing the long double **o** sound of **ew** and **ue**

Looking at oo

In some words, **oo** has the vowel sound you hear in the word **look**.

brook   **look**   **hood**

Match each word with its picture.

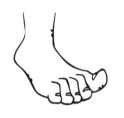

book

cookie

foot

hood

hook

wood

Underline each word with the same vowel sound as **foot**.

stood   **took**   **tooth**   **good**   **boot**   **look**

Phonics II

Some Special Words

The words in the box below all have the same vowel sound as **look**.

could	**would**	**bull**
put	**should**	**full**

The **l** in the words **could**, **would**, and **should** is silent—it has no sound.

Circle the word that best completes each sentence.

The box is _____ of pens.

full	**pull**

The big _____ has horns.

bull	**could**

You _____ be kind to pets.

should	**would**

I _____ my bike away.

pull	**put**

Completing short sentences; recognizing the short double **o** sound of **ou** and **u**

Surprise Spellings

In some words, **ie** has the long **e** sound.

ch<u>ie</u>f　　　**f<u>ie</u>ld**

bel<u>ie</u>ve　　　**p<u>ie</u>ce**

In a few words, **eigh** has the long **a** sound.

n<u>eigh</u>bor　　**<u>eigh</u>t**　　　**sl<u>eigh</u>**　　　**w<u>eigh</u>**

Circle the word that best completes each sentence.

I live next door to my ___. | neighbor　　chief

Look how much I ___! | eight　　weigh

Flowers grow in that ___. | field　　piece

Recognizing irregular spellings of the **a** and **e** long vowel sounds

The Joyful Noise of oi and oy!

Both **oi** and **oy** have the same vowel sound.

b<u>oy</u>

 b<u>oi</u>l

Underline **oi** or **oy** in each word.

oil   choice   noise   point

join   annoy   toy   joy

Rewrite the **oi** and **oy** words in each sentence on the lines below.

The boy will boil a hot dog.

_____   _____

An oyster is not noisy.

_____   _____

Point to the cowboy.

_____   _____

And Now About ow and ou

Both **ow** and **ou** can have the same vowel sound.

br<u>ow</u>n  r<u>ou</u>nd

Underline **ow** or **ou** in each word.

how   about   loud   flower

cowboy   house   down   mouth   found

Rewrite the **ow** and **ou** words in each sentence on the lines below.

The clown likes to laugh and shout.

_____   _____

The cowboy sniffs the flower.

_____   _____

Now we will sit on the ground.

_____   _____

Ought We to Trust ou?

There are different sounds for **ou**. Say each word below and listen for the **ou** sound.

c**ou**ld	c**ou**ch	c**ou**gh

When **ou** is followed by **ght**, the **gh** is silent and only the **t** is heard.

She b**ou**ght skates

Color the two boxes in each row whose words share the same **ou** sound.

about	ought	bought
would	found	could
mouth	out	would
cough	fought	should

Recognizing multiple sounds of **ou**

Check out ch

The sound for **ch** is heard at the beginning of **<u>ch</u>air** and at the end of **bran<u>ch</u>**.

<u>ch</u>air     **bran<u>ch</u>**

Write **ch** to complete each word. Match each word with its picture.

_____eck

ben_____

_____est

tea_____er

_____ain

in_____

_____ief

_____ur_____

Phonics II

Showing Off sh

The sound for **sh** is heard at the beginning of **<u>sh</u>oe** and at the end of **fi<u>sh</u>**.

<u>sh</u>oe

 **fi<u>sh</u>**

Write **sh** to complete each word. Match each word with its picture.

_____irt

di_____

fla_____

bu_____

_____apes

tra_____

_____op

_____ark

Recognizing the sound of the consonant digraph **sh**

Two Sounds of th

One sound for **th** is heard in the words **the** and **mother**.

The other sound for **th** is heard in the words **thirty** and **teeth**.

 mother

 teeth

Read each word on the left aloud. If it has the same **th** sound as **mother**, circle the 👩. If it has the same **th** sound as **thirty**, circle the **30**.

thing	👩	**30**
thin	👩	**30**
there	👩	**30**
then	👩	**30**
thick	👩	**30**
father	👩	**30**

Phonics II

Recognizing the two sounds of the consonant digraph **th**: voiced and unvoiced

What's Up with wh?

The sound for **wh** is heard at the beginning of the word **wh**eel.

Read each sentence. Draw a line to the missing **wh** word.

whale
What
wheat
Where
Which
while
white

The girl sat ____ she ate.

A ____ lives in the sea.

Some farmers grow ____.

Snow is ____.

____ did you say?

____ did my dog go?

____ toy do you want?

Using ng

The sound for **ng** is heard at the end of **ki<u>ng</u>** and **ba<u>ng</u>**.

ki<u>ng</u>  **ba<u>ng</u>**

Write **ng** to complete each word. Match each word with its picture.

wi_____

ri_____

swi_____

wro_____

fi_____**er**

si_____

What Do You See?

Read the word in each space. Color the picture using the code.

ch words = blue   **sh** words = green   **ng** words = pink

wh words = brown   **th** words = yellow

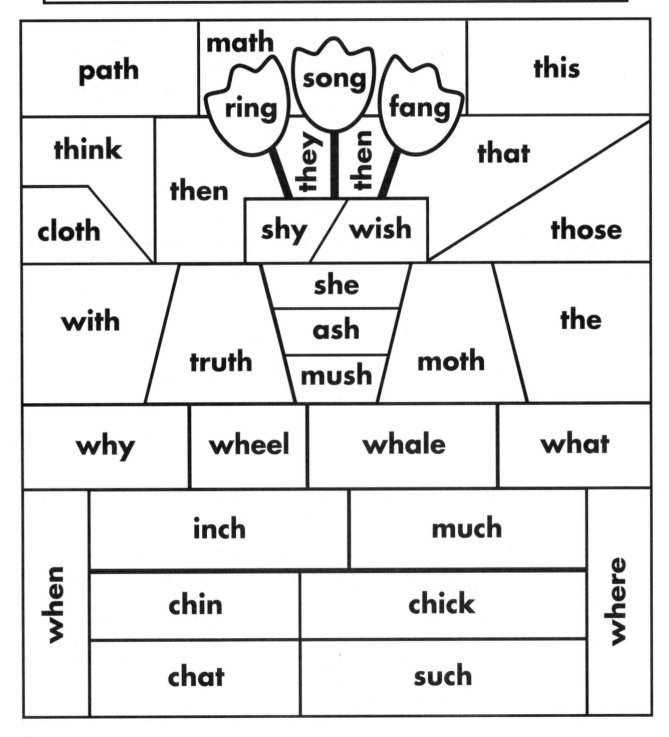

Reviewing the sounds of consonant digraphs

Answer Key

As the child completes the pages in this section, review his or her answers. When you take the time to correct the work and explain mistakes, you're showing your child that you feel learning is important.

page 187

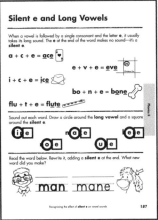

Silent e and Long Vowels

When a vowel is followed by a single consonant and the letter **e**, it usually takes its long sound. The **e** at the end of the word makes no sound—it's a **silent e**.

a + c + e = **ace**

e + v + e = **eve**

i + c + e = **ice**

bo + n + e = **bone**

flu + t + e = **flute**

Sound out each word. Draw a circle around the **long vowel** and a square around the **silent e**.

Read the word below. Rewrite it, adding a **silent e** at the end. What new word did you make?

man mane

Recognizing the effect of silent e on vowel words 187

page 188

Silent e Word Play

Say the name of each picture. Fill in the missing vowel and the **silent e** to complete the word.

rope

cake

cube

dice

stove

hive

Cross out the **silent e** at the end each word. Sound out the new words that you made.

finX hugX madX notX

188 *Recognizing the effect of silent e on vowel words*

page 189

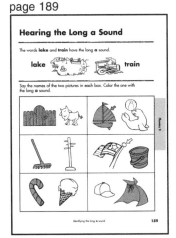

Hearing the Long a Sound

The words **lake** and **train** have the long **a** sound.

lake   train

Say the names of the two pictures in each box. Color the one with the long **a** sound.

Identifying the long a sound 189

page 190

Strain Your Brain!

Usually, **ai** has the long **a** sound.

nail   **braid**

Write words from the box to complete each sentence. Circle **ai** in each word you write.

| hail | rain | mail | pail | paint | laid |

The _____ pail _____ is full of

_____ paint _____.

Will the _____ bring _____ rain

or _____ hail _____?

I _____ laid _____ the

_____ mail _____ on the table.

190 *Recognizing and writing words with long a spelled ai*

page 191

Another Way to Make Long a

Usually, **ay** has the long **a** sound.

hay   **tray**

Write words from the box to complete each sentence. Circle **ay** in each word you write.

| clay | pay | day | play | gray | stay |

Every _____ day _____ I

_____ play _____ with friends.

I _____ stay _____ inside when

the clouds are _____ gray _____.

Did you _____ pay _____

for the _____ clay _____?

Recognizing and writing words with long a spelled ay 191

page 192

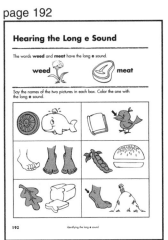

Hearing the Long e Sound

The words **weed** and **meat** have the long **e** sound.

weed   meat

Say the names of the two pictures in each box. Color the one with the long **e** sound.

192 *Identifying the long e sound*

page 193

Neat!

Usually, **ea** has the long **e** sound.

leaf   **seal**

Write words from the box to complete each sentence. Circle **ea** in each word you write.

| meal | eat | tea | team | leap | cream |

We will _____ eat _____ our

_____ meal _____ now.

Everyone on the _____ team _____

can _____ leap _____ high.

I put _____ cream _____

in my _____ tea _____.

Recognizing and writing words with long e spelled ea 193

page 194

We Keep Up with e

When the only vowel in a word is one **e** at the end, that **e** usually has a long sound.

be **he** **she** **me** **we**

Usually, **ee** has the long **e** sound.

knee   **meet**

Circle the word that completes each sentence.

Spring will _____ here soon.
| be | he | me |

Cars drive on the _____.
| sleep | steep | street |

How far can you _____?
| see | seem | sheep |

A _____ is on the flower.
| feet | beef | bee |

I _____ happy today.
| fee | feel | free |

194 *Completing short sentences; recognizing words with long e spelled e and ee*

page 195

Hearing the Long i Sound

The words **kite** and **light** have the long **i** sound.

kite   light

Say the names of the two pictures in each box. Color the one with the long **i** sound.

Identifying the long i sound 195

page 196

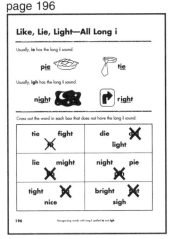

Like, Lie, Light—All Long i

Usually, **ie** has the long **i** sound.

pie   **tie**

Usually, **igh** has the long **i** sound.

night   **right**

Cross out the word in each box that does not have the long **i** sound.

tie fightX	dieX light
lieX might	nightX pie
tight niceX	bright sighX

196 *Recognizing words with long i spelled ie and igh*

page 197

Hearing the Long o Sound

The words **nose** and **coat** have the long **o** sound.

nose   coat

Say the names of the two pictures in each box. Color the one with the long **o** sound.

Identifying the long o sound 197

page 198

Partners with o

Usually, **oe** at the end of a word has the long **o** sound.

doe   **hoe**

Usually, **oa** has the long **o** sound.

coast   **float**

Match each word with its picture.

toe
boat
coal
toast
soap
coat

198 *Recognizing words with long o spelled oe and oa*

Which Long o Word Fits?

When **o** is at the end of a word, it often takes its long sound.

"Ho, ho, ho!"

In many words, **ow** has the long **o** sound.

bow • • • • **snow**

Circle the long **o** word that best completes each sentence.

We will ___ to the store.
no (go) so

A big, black ___ is on the roof.
row low (crow)

Did the wind ___ the tree down?
mow (blow) throw

I like to sleep in my ___ bed.
(own) blown grown

Completing short sentences; recognizing words with long o spelled o and ow 199

Hearing the Long u Sound

The words **mule** and **fruit** have the long **u** sound.

mule • • fruit

Say the names of the two pictures in each box. Color the one with the long **u** sound.

200 Identifying the long u sound

Partners with u

Usually, **ue** has the long **u** sound.

glue • • Tuesday

In some words, **ui** has the long **u** sound.

fruit • • Juice

Match each word with its picture.

fruit
clue
glue
bruise
cruise
suit

Recognizing words with long u spelled ue and ui 201

Y as a Vowel

The letter **y** can be used as a vowel as well as a consonant. Sometimes it has the long **i** sound, as in **fly**.

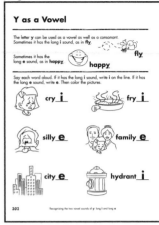 fly

Sometimes it has the long **e** sound, as in **happy**.

happy

Say each word aloud. If it has the long **i** sound, write **i** on the line. If it has the long **e** sound, write **e**. Then color the pictures.

cry **i**   fry **i**

silly **e**   family **e**

city **e**   hydrant **i**

202 Recognizing the two vowel sounds of y: long i and long e

Are You Ready for ar?

Usually, **ar** has the vowel sound you hear in **barn**.

barn

Circle the correct name for each picture.

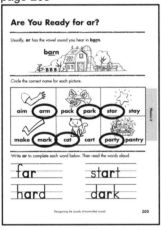
aim (arm) pack (park) (star) stay
make (mark) cat cart (party) pantry

Write **ar** to complete each word below. Then read the words aloud.

far   start
hard   dark

Recognizing the sounds of r-controlled vowels 203

Don't Forget or!

Usually, **or** has the vowel sound you hear in **fork**.

fork

Circle the correct name for each picture.

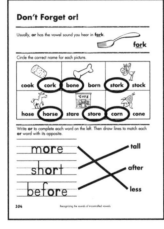
cook (cork) (bone) born (stork) stock
hose (horse) stare (store) (corn) cone

Write **or** to complete each word on the left. Then draw lines to match each **or** word with its opposite.

more — tall
short — after
before — less

204 Recognizing the sounds of r-controlled vowels

The Early Bird Gets the Worm

The vowel sound is the same in each of the words below.

bird   worm   turn   fern   earth

The **ar** in **backward** also has this vowel sound.

backward

Write five different letter pairs that can have the same vowel sound that you hear in **earth**.

ir   or
ur   er   ar

Circle the words that have the same vowel sound that you hear in **earth**.

(nurse) (fur) four (forward)
(burn) more (girl) (word)

Recognizing the sounds of r-controlled vowels 205

Different Letters, Same Sound

Usually, **aw** has the vowel sound you hear in the word **saw**.

saw

Often, **al** has the same sound.

call   talk

Use the words in the box to write the name of each picture.

salt   walk   ball   yawn   paw   hawk

ball   walk
yawn   hawk

206 Recognizing the vowel sounds of a/consonant combinations

A Moose on the Moon

In some words, **oo** has the vowel sound you hear in **moon**.

moon
moose
food

Match each word with its picture.

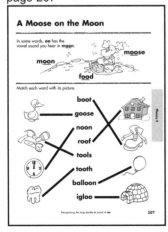
boot
goose
noon
roof
tools
tooth
balloon
igloo

Recognizing the long double o sound of oo 207

Let's Buy Some New Glue

Often, **ew** and **ue** have the same vowel sound as the **oo** in **moon**.

New Glue on Sale!

new   glue

Choose a word that best completes each sentence and write it on the line.

When will the tulips **bloom** ?
blew bloom blue

Ron **drew** a picture.
drew droop due

Mom put meat in the **stew**.
clue gloom stew

Anna **threw** the ball.
true threw troop

208 Completing short sentences; recognizing the long double o sound of ew and ue

Looking at oo

In some words, **oo** has the vowel sound you hear in the word **look**.

look   hood
brook

Match each word with its picture.

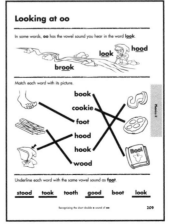
book
cookie
foot
hood
hook
wood

Underline each word with the same vowel sound as **foot**.

stood   took   tooth   good   boot   look

Recognizing the short double o sound of oo 209

Some Special Words

The words in the box below all have the same vowel sound as **look**.

could   would   bull
put   should   full

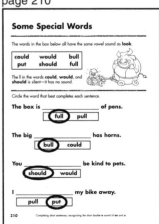

The **l** in the words **could**, **would**, and **should** is silent—it has no sound.

Circle the word that best completes each sentence.

The box is ___ of pens.
(full) pull

The big ___ has horns.
(bull) could

You ___ be kind to pets.
(should) would

I ___ my bike away.
pull (put)

210 Completing short sentences; recognizing the short double o sound of oo and u

Surprise Spellings

In some words, **ie** has the long **e** sound.

chief   **field**   be**lieve**   **piece**

In a few words, **eigh** has the long **a** sound.

neighbor   **eight**   **sleigh**   **weigh**

Circle the word that best completes each sentence.

I live next door to my ___. ⟨**neighbor**⟩ chief

Look how much I ___! eight ⟨**weigh**⟩

Flowers grow in that ___. ⟨**field**⟩ piece

Recognizing irregular spellings of the a and e long vowel sounds   211

The Joyful Noise of oi and oy!

Both **oi** and **oy** have the same vowel sound.

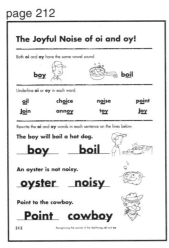

b**oy**   b**oil**

Underline **oi** or **oy** in each word.

oil   ch**oi**ce   n**oi**se   p**oi**nt
J**oi**n   ann**oy**   t**oy**   J**oy**

Rewrite the **oi** and **oy** words in each sentence on the lines below.

The boy will boil a hot dog.

boy   **boil**

An oyster is not noisy.

oyster   **noisy**

Point to the cowboy.

Point   **cowboy**

212   Recognizing the sounds of the diphthongs oi and oy

And Now About ow and ou

Both **ow** and **ou** can have the same vowel sound.

br**ow**n   r**ou**nd

Underline **ow** or **ou** in each word.

h**ow**   ab**ou**t   l**ou**d   fl**ow**er
c**ow**boy   h**ou**se   d**ow**n   m**ou**th   f**ou**nd

Rewrite the **ow** and **ou** words in each sentence on the lines below.

The clown likes to laugh and shout.

clown   **shout**

The cowboy sniffs the flower.

cowboy   **flower**

Now we will sit on the ground.

Now   **ground**

Recognizing the sounds of the diphthongs ow and ou   213

Ought We to Trust ou?

There are different sounds for **ou**. Say each word below and listen for the **ou** sound.

could   couch   cough

When **ou** is followed by **ght**, the **gh** is silent and only the **t** is heard.

She bought skates

Color the two boxes in each row whose words share the same **ou** sound.

about	ought	bought
would	found	could
mouth	out	would
cough	fought	should

214   Recognizing multiple sounds of ou

Check out ch

The sound for **ch** is heard at the beginning of **chair** and at the end of **branch**.

chair   **branch**

Write **ch** to complete each word. Match each word with its picture.

check
ben**ch**
chest
tea**ch**er
chain
in**ch**
chief
chur**ch**

Recognizing the sound of the consonant digraph ch   215

Showing Off sh

The sound for **sh** is heard at the beginning of **shoe** and at the end of **fish**.

shoe   **fish**

Write **sh** to complete each word. Match each word with its picture.

shirt
di**sh**
fla**sh**
bu**sh**
shapes
tra**sh**
shop
shark

216   Recognizing the sound of the consonant digraph sh

Two Sounds of th

One sound for **th** is heard in the words **the** and **mother**.

mother

The other sound for **th** is heard in the words **thirty** and **teeth**.

teeth

Read each word on the left aloud. If it has the same **th** sound as **mother**, circle the ☺. If it has the same **th** sound as **thirty**, circle the **30**.

thing	☺	⟨30⟩
thin	☺	⟨30⟩
there	⟨☺⟩	30
then	⟨☺⟩	30
thick	☺	⟨30⟩
father	⟨☺⟩	30

Recognizing the two sounds of the consonant digraph th: voiced and unvoiced   217

What's Up with wh?

The sound for **wh** is heard at the beginning of the word **wheel**.

Read each sentence. Draw a line to the missing **wh** word.

whale
What
wheat
Where
Which
while
white

The girl sat ___ she ate.
A ___ lives in the sea.
Some farmers grow ___.
Snow is ___.
___ did you say?
___ did my dog go?
___ toy do you want?

218   Completing short sentences, recognizing the sound of the consonant digraph wh

Phonics II

Using ng

The sound for **ng** is heard at the end of **king** and **bang**.

king   **bang**

Write **ng** to complete each word. Match each word with its picture.

wi**ng**
ri**ng**
swi**ng**
wro**ng**
fi**ng**er
si**ng**

Recognizing the sound of the consonant digraph ng   219

What Do You See?

Read the word in each space. Color the picture using the code.

ch words = blue   **sh** words = green   **ng** words = pink
wh words = brown   **th** words = yellow

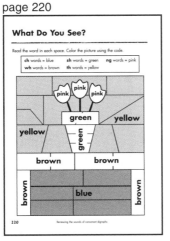

pink   pink   pink
green   yellow
yellow   green
brown   brown
brown   blue   brown

220   Reviewing the sounds of consonant digraphs

Answers

It Has a Name!

A word that names a person, place, or thing is called a **noun**.

mother
person

home
place

purse
thing

My **mother** went **home** to get her **purse**.

Use the **nouns** in the box to write the name of each picture.
Then color the pictures.

girl	car	barn	hat

_____

- - - - - - - - - - - - - -

_____

_____

- - - - - - - - - - - - - -

_____

_____

- - - - - - - - - - - - - -

_____

_____

- - - - - - - - - - - - - -

_____

Recognizing nouns

Which Ones Are Nouns?

Nouns are words that name people, places, and things.

Circle all the **nouns** in the word box.

hen	farmer	barn	if
and	green	sun	tree

Draw a picture of one of the **nouns** from the box in the space below. Write the **noun** below the picture.

Grammar & Writing Skills I

Searching for Nouns

Circle all the **nouns** in each sentence.

The turtle lives in a pond.

The monkey has a tail.

The giraffe eats leaves.

A zebra has stripes.

The pilot sees a bird.

Ants make hills.

Identifying nouns in sentences

The First Day of School

Write a **noun** from the box to complete each sentence.

teacher	school	bell	pencil	desks

_____

The _____ rings.

_____

_____ has begun.

The _____ smiles.

The girls and boys sit at _____ .

Ann writes with a _____ .

How Many?

To make many **nouns** mean "more than one," add **s** at the end.
A **noun** that names "more than one" is a **plural noun**.

one bear

three bears

Look at the picture. Then read the questions and circle the answers.

1. Look for a cap. How many do you see?

| one cap | two caps | three caps |

2. Look for a rope. How many do you see?

| one rope | two ropes | three ropes |

3. Look for a mat. How many do you see?

| one mat | two mats | three mats |

4. Look for a ball. How many do you see?

| one ball | two balls | three balls |

Forming plurals of regular nouns by adding **s**

Animal or Animals

Read the word under each picture.
If it's a **noun**, write it on the **ANIMAL** list.
If it's a **plural noun**, write it on the **ANIMALS** list.

birds

pig

cats

lion

dogs

tiger

ANIMAL	**ANIMALS**

Not Just One

Ad **es** to a **noun** ending in **s**, **x**, **ch**, or **sh** to make it a **plural noun**.

one dress

two dress<u>es</u>

one fox

two fox<u>es</u>

Rewrite each **noun**, adding **es** at the end to make it **plural**.

match

_____

- - - - - - - - - - - - - - -

_____

bus

_____

- - - - - - - - - - - - - - -

_____

brush

_____

- - - - - - - - - - - - - - -

_____

box

_____

- - - - - - - - - - - - - - -

_____

Adding **-es** to form plurals of nouns ending in **s**, **x**, **ch**, and **sh**

One and More Than One

Read the **nouns** inside the ◇s. Circle the correct **plural** form of each one.

watch
watches
watchs

truck
truckes
trucks

broom
brooms
broomes

bug
buges
bugs

six
sixs
sixes

dish
dishes
dishs

glass
glasses
glasss

pail
pails
pailes

Watch Out for y

Sometimes **y** comes after a consonant at the end of a **noun**.
To make these nouns **plural**, change the **y** to **i** and add **es**.

one bunny bunn~~y~~ⁱ + es = bunnies **two bunnies**

Rewrite each **noun** to make it **plural**.

candy

fly

baby

berry

kitty

lady

Forming plurals of nouns ending in **y** after a consonant

Making Plurals

Read the **nouns** inside the ◇s. Circle the correct **plural** form of each one.

daisy — daisies / daisys

cherry — cherries / cherryes

lunch — lunchs / lunches

fly — flies / flyes

fox — foxs / foxes

city — cityes / cities

chick — chickes / chicks

puppy — puppies / puppys

Grammar & Writing Skills I

Noun Search

Read the **nouns** and their **plural** forms. Then find and circle them in the puzzle. The words may go across or down.

baby	ball	box	snake	fly
babies	balls	boxes	snakes	flies

a b a l l s b

b o x e s n o

a b a b y a a

b x s n a k e

i b o x f e f

e f l i e s l

s b a l l d y

Special Plurals

Some **nouns** have a special **plural** form.

One	More Than One
man	men
woman	women
child	children
mouse	mice
foot	feet
tooth	teeth

Write the **plural** form of the **noun** in the box to complete each sentence.

I have two _____ . **foot**

Both _____ can swim. **child**

The _____ like the maze. **mouse**

Two _____ wrote the song. **man**

I brush my _____ . **tooth**

Three _____ baked pies. **woman**

Grammar & Writing Skills I

More Special Plurals

A few **nouns** do not change in their **plural** form.

One	More Than One
deer	deer
fish	fish
moose	moose
scissors	scissors
sheep	sheep

Look at the picture clues. Write the missing **plural noun** in each sentence.

Many _____ live in the park.

Luis saw two _____ in the woods.

The _____ eat grass.

Feed the _____ before lunch.

Use _____ to cut paper.

Recognizing irregular plurals

What is a Verb?

A **verb** is a word that tells what a person or thing does.

run     **spin**

Match each picture with its **verb**.

march

sing

dance

clap

Circle the **verb** to complete each sentence.

The bell _____.

| soft | rings |

The cat _____.

| purrs | top |

Where is the Verb?

A **verb** is a word that tells what a person or thing does.

The sun **shines**.

Circle the **verb** in each sentence.

Ships sail on the sea.

She sits in the sun.

Waves roll in.

They play a game.

He throws a ball.

Recognizing verbs in sentences

Bears in Space

A **verb** usually ends in **s** when it tells about only one.
It usually does not end in **s** when it tells about more than one.

One star **twinkle<u>s</u>**.   Stars **twinkle**.

Circle the correct **verb** to
complete each sentence.
Then color the picture.

Young Bear _____ **a helmet.**

wear	wears

Mom and Dad Bear _____ **photos.**

take	takes

They all _____ **in space.**

floats	float

Young Bear _____ **space.**

likes	like

Mom and Dad Bear _____ **space, too.**

likes	like

Choosing the correct verb form to agree in number with the subject

Pretty as a Picture

A **verb** ending in **s** usually tells about one person or thing.
A **verb** not ending in **s** usually tells about more than one.

One bird sings.   **Three birds sing.**

Read the first sentence in each row and underline the verb.
Rewrite the verb to fit the second sentence.

One ant crawls. Many ants _____.

Many ducks swim. One duck _____.

One bunny hops. Many bunnies _____.

Many flowers grow. One flower _____.

Writing the correct verb form to agree in number with the subject

Which is Correct?

Fill in the ○ by the sentence that uses the correct **verb**.

○The children like art.
○The children likes art.

○A girl paint.
○A girl paints.

○A boy use clay.
○A boy uses clay.

○Two boys draw cars.
○Two boys draws cars.

○The teacher hangs up the art.
○The teacher hang up the art.

○They all works hard.
○They all work hard.

Choosing the correct verb form to agree in number with the subject

Am, Are, and Is

Verbs may also tell what a person or thing is. We use the verbs **am**, **are**, and **is** to do this.

Verb Chart

I– – – – – – – – – –	**am**
You – – – – – – – –	**are**
He, She, or It – – –	**is**
We – – – – – – – –	**are**
They – – – – – – –	**are**

Use **am** with **I** when you tell about yourself.

I **am** happy!

Use **is** with **he**, **she**, or **it** when you tell about another person or thing.

He **is** happy!

Use **are** with **you** or when you tell about more than one.

The dogs **are** happy!

Write **am**, **are**, or **is** to complete each sentence.

Leaves _____ **green.**   **I** _____ **smart.**

Nan _____ **a girl.**   **Candy** _____ **sweet.**

We _____ **friends.**   **You** _____ **nice.**

Using **am**, **are** and **is**: present tense forms of the verb **to be**

You Are Smart!

Fill in the ◯ by the sentence that uses the correct **verb**.

◯I am your friend.
◯I is your friend.

◯You is the winner!
◯You are the winner!

◯Brian is a good kicker.
◯Brian are a good kicker.

◯The puppy is tiny.
◯The puppy are tiny.

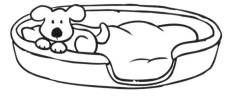

◯We are sleepy.
◯We is sleepy.

Using **am**, **are** and **is**: present tense forms of the verb **to be**

Has and Have

Verbs may also tell what a person or thing has.
We use the verbs **has** and **have** to do this.

Use **has** with **he, she**, or **it**.
Use **has** with a noun that names one.

He **has** a tail.
The squirrel **has** a tail.

Use **have** with **I, you, we**, or **they**.
Use **have** with a plural noun.

We **have** tails!

They **have** tails.
The squirrels **have** tails.

has	have
he, she, it	I, you, we, they
noun	plural noun

Fill in the ◯ by the sentence that uses the correct **verb**.

◯ A dog **has** a tail.
◯ A dog **have** a tail.

◯ I **has** a nose.
◯ I **have** a nose.

◯ We **have** gum.
◯ We **has** gum.

◯ Birds **has** wings.
◯ Birds **have** wings.

Using **has** and **have**: present tense forms of the verb **to have**

Have Fun!

Write **has** or **have** to complete each sentence.

The panda _____ a baby.

Nuts _____ hard shells.

He _____ broken the law.

The shaker _____ salt in it.

The crabs _____ claws.

Does and Do

Use **does** with **he**, **she**, or **it**.
Use **does** with a noun that names one.

He **does** his job.
The man **does** his job.

Use **do** with **I**, **you**, **we**, or **they**.
Use **do** with a plural noun.

"You **do** a good job!"

They **do** good work.
The people **do** good work.

does	do
he, she, it	I, you, we, they
noun	plural noun

Write **does** or **do** to complete each sentence.

Cats _____ **purr.**

She _____ **tricks.**

I _____ **my homework.**

Tim _____ **his chores.**

Using **does** and **do**: present tense forms of the verb **to do**

Do Your Best!

Write **does** or **do** to complete each sentence.

This hat _____ not have stripes.

Fairies _____ magic.

Mom _____ like to read.

Clowns _____ funny tricks.

Ann _____ skate well.

Grammar & Writing Skills I

Using **does** and **do**: present tense forms of the verb **to do**

Let's Go Shopping!

Circle the **verb** that correctly completes each sentence.

Many people (**come** / **comes**) to the store.

He **set** / **sets** food on the shelf.

Dad **chooses** / **choose** a box.

The cart **has** / **have** wheels.

The clerk **does** / **do** her job.

Dad **carries** / **carry** the bag.

Present tense verb-subject agreement review

Let's Go to the Zoo!

Write a **noun** or **verb** from the box to complete each sentence.

ape	bear	made	went	were

_____verb_____

- - - - - - - - - - -

We _____ to the zoo.

_____noun_____

- - - - - - - - - - -

I waved to the _____ .

_____verb_____

- - - - - - - - - - -

The monkeys _____ me laugh.

_____noun_____

- - - - - - - - - - -

The _____ was asleep.

_____verb_____

- - - - - - - - - - -

The hippos _____ fat.

Grammar & Writing Skills I

Let's Go to the Movies!

Write a **noun** or **verb** from the box to complete each sentence.

box	buy	is	meet	seats

verb
_____

Rita and Tom _____ at the door.

verb
_____

They _____ tickets.

noun
_____

They buy a _____ of popcorn.

noun
_____

They choose their _____ .

verb
_____

The movie _____ funny.

Completing sentences with nouns and verbs

Fish Story

Read the short story or have someone read it to you. Circle all the **nouns**. Underline all the **verbs**.

Hal likes to fish in the brook. The water is clean. The water is cold. There are lots of fish in the water.

Hal feels a fish tug the line. Hal catches the fish. Then he puts it back into the clean, cold water. It is too small to keep.

Pete and Pat

Read the short story or have someone read it to you. Circle each correct **noun** or **verb**. Then color Pete and Pat.

Pete (has have) a dog. The dog (is am) tan. Her name is Pat.

Pat (like likes) to run. Her (tail tails) wags when she (run runs). Pat likes to chew (bone bones). Pete (give gives) her a bone every (day dry). Pat likes to (plays play). Pete throws a (ball bull) to her. Pat likes that (game gum).

Pat (love loves) Pete. Pete (loves love) Pat. They are good (friends friend).

Completing a short story with nouns and verbs

Answer Key

As the child completes the pages in this section, review his or her answers. When you take the time to correct the work and explain mistakes, you're showing your child that you feel learning is important.

page 224

It Has a Name!

A word that names a person, place, or thing is called a **noun**.

mother person **home** place **purse** thing

My **mother** went **home** to get her **purse**.

Use the **nouns** in the box to write the name of each picture. Then color the pictures.

| girl | car | barn | hat |

car

hat

barn

girl

224　　　Recognizing nouns

page 225

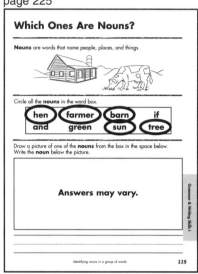

Which Ones Are Nouns?

Nouns are words that name people, places, and things.

Circle all the **nouns** in the word box.

(hen) (farmer) (barn) if
and green (sun) (tree)

Draw a picture of one of the **nouns** from the box in the space below. Write the **noun** below the picture.

Answers may vary.

Identifying nouns in a group of words　　　225

page 226

Searching for Nouns

Circle all the **nouns** in each sentence.

The (turtle) lives in a (pond).

The (monkey) has a (tail).

The (giraffe) eats (leaves).

(zebra) has (stripes).

The (pilot) sees a (bird).

(Ants) make (hills).

226　　　Identifying nouns in sentences

page 227

The First Day of School

Write a **noun** from the box to complete each sentence.

| teacher | school | bell | pencil | desks |

The ___bell___ rings.

___School___ has begun.

The ___teacher___ smiles.

The girls and boys sit at ___desks___.

Ann writes with a ___pencil___.

Using nouns to complete sentences　　　227

page 228

How Many?

To make many **nouns** mean "more than one" add **s** at the end. A **noun** that names "more than one" is a **plural noun**.

one bear　　**three bears**

Look at the picture. Then read the questions and circle the answers.

1. Look for a cap. How many do you see?
one cap　　two caps　　(three caps)

2. Look for a rope. How many do you see?
(one rope)　　two ropes　　three ropes

3. Look for a mat. How many do you see?
one mat　　(two mats)　　three mats

4. Look for a ball. How many do you see?
one ball　　(two balls)　　three balls

228　　　Forming plurals of regular nouns by adding s

page 229

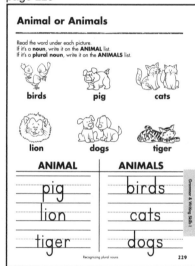

Animal or Animals

Read the word under each picture.
If it's a **noun**, write it on the **ANIMAL** list.
If it's a **plural noun**, write it on the **ANIMALS** list.

birds　　**pig**　　**cats**

lion　　**dogs**　　**tiger**

ANIMAL	ANIMALS
pig	birds
lion	cats
tiger	dogs

Recognizing plural nouns　　　229

page 230

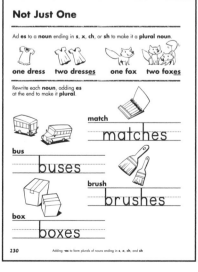

Not Just One

Add **es** to a **noun** ending in **s**, **x**, **ch**, or **sh** to make it a **plural noun**.

one dress　　**two dresses**　　**one fox**　　**two foxes**

Rewrite each **noun**, adding **es** at the end to make it **plural**.

match
matches

bus
buses

brush
brushes

box
boxes

230　　　Adding -es to form plurals of nouns ending in s, x, ch, and sh

page 231

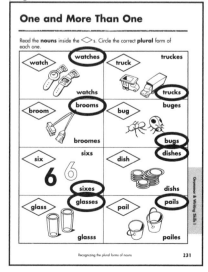

One and More Than One

Read the **nouns** inside the ◇ s. Circle the correct **plural** form of each one.

watch (watches) truckes

watchs (trucks)

broom (brooms) buges

broomes (bugs)

six sixs dish (dishes)

(sixes) dishs

glass (glasses) pail (pails)

glasss pailes

Recognizing the plural forms of nouns　　　231

page 232

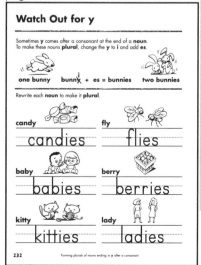

Watch Out for y

Sometimes **y** comes after a consonant at the end of a **noun**. To make these nouns **plural**, change the **y** to **i** and add **es**.

one bunny　　bunn(y→i) + **es** = **bunnies**　　**two bunnies**

Rewrite each **noun** to make it **plural**.

candy
candies

fly
flies

baby
babies

berry
berries

kitty
kitties

lady
ladies

232　　　Forming plurals of nouns ending in y after a consonant

Making Plurals

Read the **nouns** inside the ◇s. Circle the correct **plural** form of each one.

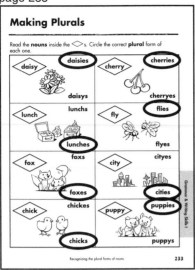

- ◇ daisy — **daisies**, daisys
- ◇ cherry — **cherries**, cherryes
- ◇ lunch — lunchs, **lunches**
- ◇ fly — **flies**, flyes
- ◇ fox — foxs, **foxes**
- ◇ city — **cities**, cityes
- ◇ chick — chickes, **chicks**
- ◇ puppy — **puppies**, puppys

Recognizing the plural forms of nouns   233

Noun Search

Read the **nouns** and their **plural** forms. Then find and circle them in the puzzle. The words may go across or down.

baby	ball	box	snake	fly
babies	balls	boxes	snakes	flies

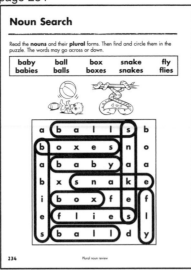

```
a  b  a  l  l  s  b
b  o  x  e  s  n  o
a  b  a  b  y  a  a
b  x  s  n  a  k  e
i  b  o  x  f  e  f
e  f  l  i  e  s  l
s  b  a  l  l  d  y
```

234   Plural noun review

Special Plurals

Some **nouns** have a special **plural** form.

One	More Than One
man	men
woman	women
child	children
mouse	mice
foot	feet
tooth	teeth

Write the **plural** form of the **noun** in the box to complete each sentence.

I have two **feet**. [foot]

Both **children** can swim. [child]

The **mice** like the maze. [mouse]

Two **me** wrote the song. [man]

I brush my **teeth**. [tooth]

Three **women** baked pies. [woman]

Recognizing irregular plurals   235

More Special Plurals

A few **nouns** do not change in their **plural** form.

One	More Than One
deer	deer
fish	fish
moose	moose
scissors	scissors
sheep	sheep

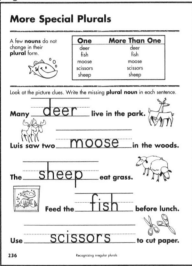

Look at the picture clues. Write the missing **plural noun** in each sentence.

Many **deer** live in the park.

Luis saw two **moose** in the woods.

The **sheep** eat grass.

Feed the **fish** before lunch.

Use **scissors** to cut paper.

236   Recognizing irregular plurals

What is a Verb?

A **verb** is a word that tells what a person or thing does.

run   spin

Match each picture with its **verb**.

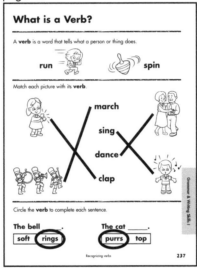

- march
- sing
- dance
- clap

Circle the **verb** to complete each sentence.

The bell ___.   soft (**rings**)

The cat ___.   (**purrs**) top

Recognizing verbs   237

Where is the Verb?

A **verb** is a word that tells what a person or thing does.

The sun **shines**.

Circle the **verb** in each sentence.

Ships (sail) on the sea.

She (sits) in the sun.

Waves (roll) in.

They (play) game.

He (throws) ball.

238   Recognizing verbs in sentences

Bears in Space

A **verb** usually ends in **s** when it tells about only one. It usually does not end in **s** when it tells about more than one.

One star **twinkles**.   Stars **twinkle**.

Circle the correct **verb** to complete each sentence. Then color the picture.

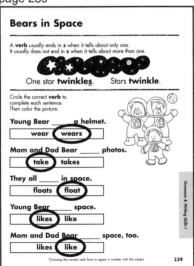

Young Bear ___ a helmet.   wear (**wears**)

Mom and Dad Bear ___ photos.   (**take**) takes

They all ___ in space.   floats (**float**)

Young Bear ___ space.   (**likes**) like

Mom and Dad Bear ___ space, too.   likes (**like**)

Choosing the correct verb form to agree in number with the subject   239

Pretty as a Picture

A **verb** ending in **s** usually tells about one person or thing. A **verb** not ending in **s** usually tells about more than one.

One bird sings.   Three birds sing.

Read the first sentence in each row and underline the verb. Rewrite the verb to fit the second sentence.

One ant <u>crawls</u>. Many ants **crawl**.

Many ducks <u>swim</u>. One duck **swims**.

One bunny <u>hops</u>. Many bunnies **hop**.

Many flowers <u>grow</u>. One flower **grows**.

240   Writing the correct verb form to agree in number with the subject

---

Which is Correct?

Fill in the ○ by the sentence that uses the correct **verb**.

- ● The children like art.
- ○ The children likes art.

- ○ A girl paint.
- ● A girl paints.

- ○ A boy use clay.
- ● A boy uses clay.

- ● Two boys draw cars.
- ○ Two boys draws cars.

- ● Teacher hangs up the art.
- ○ Teacher hang up the art.

- ○ They all works hard.
- ● They all work hard.

Choosing the correct verb form to agree in number with the subject   241

Answers

page 242

Am, Are, and Is

Verbs may also tell what a person or thing is. We use the verbs **am, are,** and **is** to do this.

Verb Chart	
I	am
You	are
He, She, or It	is
We	are
They	are

Use **am** with **I** when you tell about yourself.
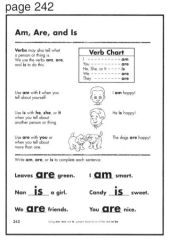
I **am** happy!

Use **is** with **he, she,** or **it** when you tell about another person or thing.
He **is** happy!

Use **are** with **you** or when you tell about more than one thing.
The dogs **are** happy!

Write **am, are,** or **is** to complete each sentence.

Leaves **are** green.   I **am** smart.

Nan **is** a girl.   Candy **is** sweet.

We **are** friends.   You **are** nice.

242   Using *am, are* and *is,* present tense forms of the verb *to be*

page 243

You Are Smart!

Fill in the ○ by the sentence that uses the correct **verb**.

● I am your friend.
○ I is your friend.

○ You is the winner!
● You are the winner!

● Brian is a good kicker.
○ Brian are a good kicker.

● The puppy is tiny.
○ The puppy are tiny.

● We are sleepy.
○ We is sleepy.

Using *am, are* and *is,* present tense forms of the verb *to be*   243

page 244

Has and Have

Verbs may also tell what a person or thing has. We use the verbs **has** and **have** to do this.

Use **has** with **he, she,** or **it**.   He **has** a tail.
Use **has** with a noun that names one.   The squirrel **has** a tail.

Use **have** with **I, you, we,** or **they**.   They **have** tails.
Use **have** with a plural noun.   The squirrels **have** tails.

has	have
he, she, it	I, you, we, they
noun	plural noun

Fill in the ○ by the sentence that uses the correct **verb**.

● A dog **has** a tail.   ○ I **has** a nose.
○ A dog **have** a tail.   ● I **have** a nose.

● We **have** gum.   ○ Birds **has** wings.
○ We **has** gum.   ● Birds **have** wings.

244   Using *has* and *have,* present tense forms of the verb *to have*

page 245

Have Fun!

Write **has** or **have** to complete each sentence.

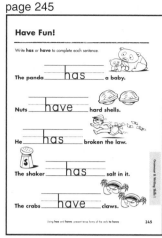

The panda **has** a baby.

Nuts **have** hard shells.

He **has** broken the law.

The shaker **has** salt in it.

The crabs **have** claws.

Using *has* and *have,* present tense forms of the verb *to have*   245

page 246

Does and Do

Use **does** with **he, she,** or **it**.   He **does** his job.
Use **does** with a noun that names one.   The man **does** his job.

Use **do** with **I, you, we,** or **they**.   They **do** good work.
Use **do** with a plural noun.   The people **do** good work.

does	do
he, she, it	I, you, we, they
noun	plural noun

Write **does** or **do** to complete each sentence.

Cats **do** purr.

She **does** tricks.

I **do** my homework.

Tim **does** his chores.

246   Using *does* and *do,* present tense forms of the verb *to do*

page 247

Do Your Best!

Write **does** or **do** to complete each sentence.

This hat **does** not have stripes.

Fairies **do** magic.

Mom **does** like to read.

Clowns **do** funny tricks.

Ann **does** skate well.

Using *does* and *do,* present tense forms of the verb *to do*   247

page 248

Let's Go Shopping!

Circle the **verb** that correctly completes each sentence.

Many people (come)/comes to the store.

He (set)/sets food on the shelf.

Dad (chooses)/choose a box.

The cart (has)/have wheels.

The clerk (does)/do her job.

Dad (carries)/carry the bag.

248   Present tense verb-subject agreement review

page 249

Let's Go to the Zoo!

Write a **noun** or **verb** from the box to complete each sentence.

ape	bear	made	went	were

verb
We **went** to the zoo.

noun
I waved to the **ape**.

verb
The monkeys **made** me laugh.

noun
The **bear** was asleep.

verb
The hippos **were** fat.

Completing sentences with nouns and verbs   249

page 250

Let's Go to the Movies!

Write a **noun** or **verb** from the box to complete each sentence.

box	buy	is	meet	seats

verb
Rita and Tom **meet** at the door.

verb
They **buy** tickets.

noun
They buy a **box** of popcorn.

noun
They choose their **seats**.

verb
The movie **is** funny.

250   Completing sentences with nouns and verbs

page 251

Fish Story

Read the short story or have someone read it to you. Circle all the **nouns**. Underline all the **verbs**.

(Hal) likes to fish in the (brook). The (water) is clean. The (water) is cold. There are lots of (fish) in the (water).

(Hal) feels a (fish) tug the (line). (Hal) catches the (fish). Then (he) puts it back into the clean, cold (water). (It) is too small to keep.

Recognizing nouns and verbs in a short story   251

page 252

Pete and Pat

Read the short story or have someone read it to you. Circle each correct **noun** or **verb**. Then color Pete and Pat.

Pete (has)/have a dog. The dog (is)/am tan. Her name is Pat.

Pat (like/(likes) to run. Her (tail)/tails wags when she (run/(runs). Pat likes to chew (bone/(bones). Pete (give/(gives) her a bone every (day)/dry. Pat likes to (play/(play) Pete throws a (ball)/bull to her. Pat likes that (game)/gum.

Pat (love/(loves) Pete. Pete (loves)/love Pat. They are good (friends)/friend.

252   Completing a short story with nouns and verbs

Words that Tell More

Some words tell more about nouns.
They are called **adjectives**.
Adjectives can answer these questions:

What kind?	How many?	What color?
fuzzy bears	**two** bears	**white** bears

Circle the **adjective** in each sentence.

This is a pretty flower.
It has two leaves.

I see tiny mice.
I see three mice.

She has long hair.
She has big eyes.

The bus is big.
The wheels are black.

Recognizing adjectives

In the Summertime

Adjectives tell more about nouns.

Write an **adjective** from the box to complete each sentence.

| big | two | black | four |

A _____ bird sings.
What color?

There are _____ clouds.
How many?

A _____ dog takes a nap.
What kind?

I see _____ squirrels.
How many?

Adjective Search

Circle two **adjectives** in each sentence.

Two  swim under deep water.

Long 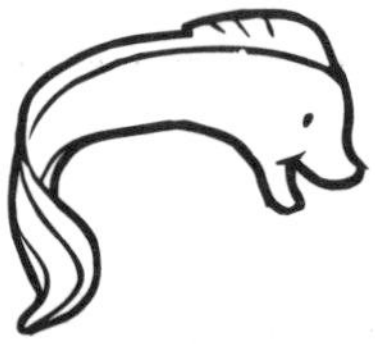s play by the old ship.

Are those round s in the open chest?

One clam sits on the smooth sand.

Tall s grow in the cool sea.

Three happy s play.

Gardening

Circle the **adjectives** in the box.

four	pretty	pea	proud
rake	neat	two	are

Write an **adjective** from the box to complete each sentence.

 works in his _____ garden.

He is _____ of his garden.

It has _____ s.

grew _____ s.

The garden is _____ and tidy.

Adjective Time

Read the words in each row. Circle the two **adjectives** that tell about the picture.

silly	icy	funny	cold

loud	wet	soft	happy

bright	cool	hot	skinny

Write an **adjective** to complete each sentence.

Soft? Nice? Hot? Kind?

_____

Summer is _____ .

_____

My friend is _____ .

_____

Pets are _____ .

_____

Games are _____ .

Adjective review

Tell About a Toy

Write the name of a toy you like in the square.
Write an **adjective** that tells about the toy in each circle.

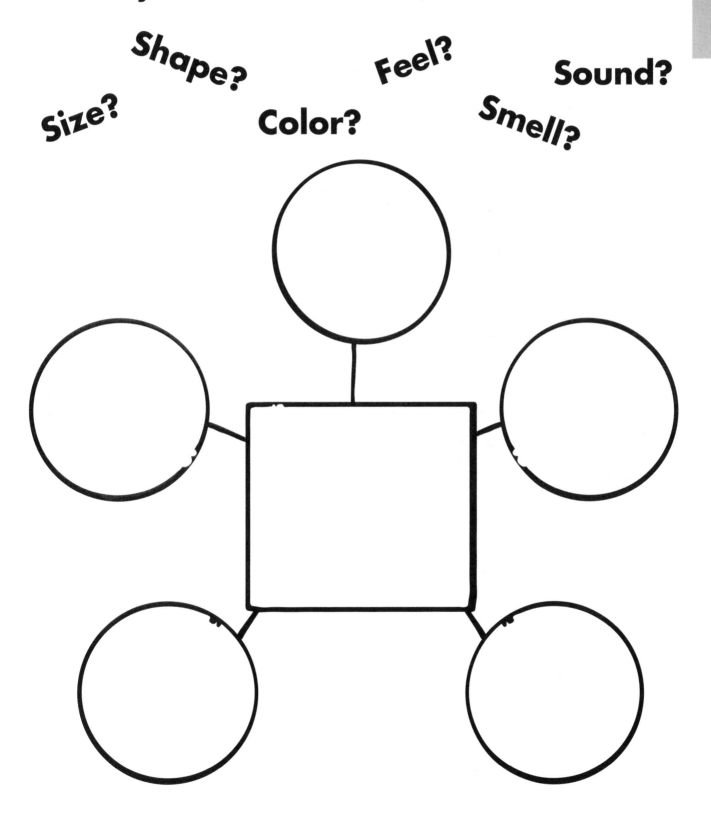

Size?   Shape?   Color?   Feel?   Smell?   Sound?

Using a graphic organizer to plan a description

Write About a Toy

On page 261 you wrote **adjectives** that tell about your toy.
Use them to write sentences about your toy on the lines below.
Then draw a picture of your toy in the box.

The name
of my toy is

Telling it All

Some sentences tell something. They are called **statements**.
A **statement** begins with a capital letter and ends with a **period**.

capital letter

The wind is strong.

period

Circle the **statement** below.

Rain fell all day.

When will the rain stop?

Fill in the ◯ by the **statement** that is written correctly.

◯ **today is a cold day.**
◯ **Today is a cold day.**

◯ **The sky is blue.**
◯ **the sky is blue.**

◯ **The children made a snowman**
◯ **The children made a snowman.**

Recognizing statements and their usage of capital letters and periods

Did You Ask Me?

Some sentences ask something. They are called **questions**. A **question** begins with a capital letter and ends with a **question mark**.

capital letter   question mark

<u>W</u>ho is it<u>?</u>

Circle the **questions**.

Where is my shoe?

Will you come with me?

The cat is in the tree.

Rewrite each **question** correctly.

what is your name

how old are you

where do you live

Jungle Questions

Color all the **questions marks** hidden in this picture red.
Then color the rest of the picture.

Visual discrimination; identifying question marks

Nice Ice

Every **statement** ends with a **period**.
Every **question** ends with a **question mark**.

Add a **period** or **question mark** to the end of each sentence.

The day is cold_____

Did the lake freeze_____

Bob has a new hat_____

Who will win the race_____

Can you ice skate_____

The dog slips_____

Reviewing punctuation usage with statements and questions

Wow!

A sentence that shows excitement is called an **exclamation**. Every **exclamation** begins with a capital letter and ends with an **exclamation point**.

capital letter

<u>W</u>atch out!

exclamation point

Circle the **exclamations** below.

I was scared!

What time is it?

I see the ice cream truck!

Ice Cream

Fill in the ◯ by the **exclamation** that is written correctly.

◯ **The soup is hot!**
◯ **the soup is hot!**

◯ **My toe hurts!**
◯ **My toe hurts.**

◯ **Look at the sunset!**
◯ **look at the sunset!**

Recognizing exclamations and their usage of capital letters and exclamation points

In the Lunch Room

Add a **period**, **question mark**, or **exclamation point** to the end of each sentence.

Lisa likes milk_____

May I sit here_____

Sam likes fruit_____

I'm so hungry_____

Why is Sam so silly_____

Hurry and eat_____

Reviewing types of sentences: statements, questions, and exclamations

Please Write!

Read this letter. Look at the names of the different parts of the letter.

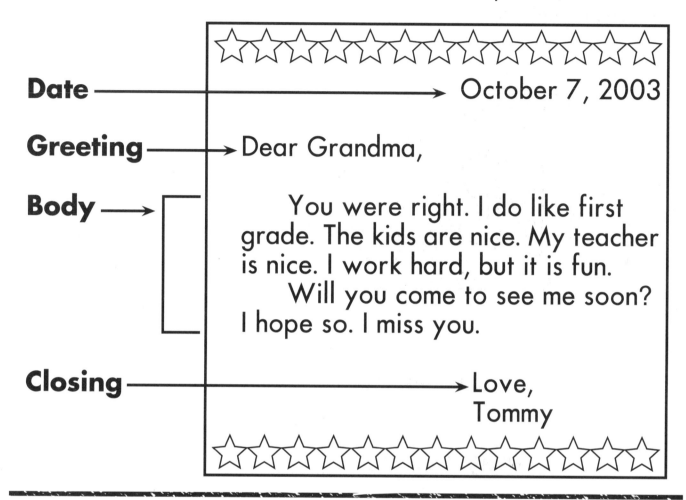

Date → October 7, 2003

Greeting → Dear Grandma,

Body →
You were right. I do like first grade. The kids are nice. My teacher is nice. I work hard, but it is fun.
Will you come to see me soon? I hope so. I miss you.

Closing →
Love,
Tommy

Circle the answer.

October 7, 2003	is the	body	date
Love,	is the	greeting	closing
I miss you.	is part of the	body	greeting
Dear Grandma,	is the	greeting	closing

Understanding the parts of a letter

Return Mail

Read this letter. Circle all the capital letters.

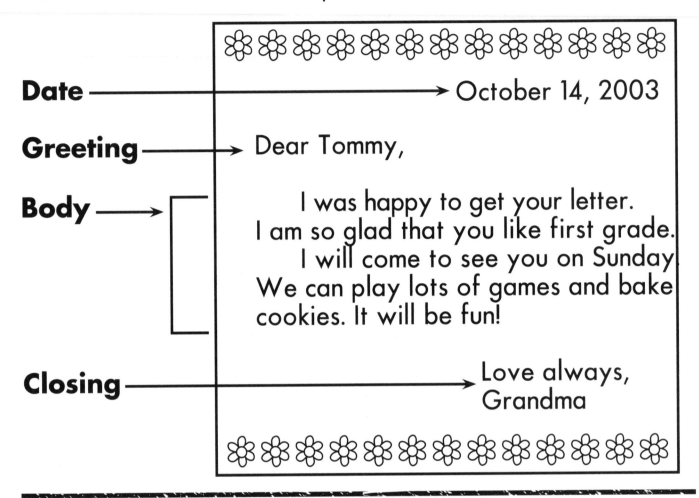

Date ⟶ October 14, 2003

Greeting ⟶ Dear Tommy,

Body ⟶ I was happy to get your letter.
I am so glad that you like first grade.
I will come to see you on Sunday.
We can play lots of games and bake
cookies. It will be fun!

Closing ⟶ Love always,
Grandma

Circle all the answers that are correct.

A capital letter is used at the beginning of:

the name of a day   **a person's name**

the name of the month   **every sentence**

the year   **the greeting**   **the closing**

Friend to Friend

Read this letter and look for the **commas**.
Circle each **comma** that you find.

comma ⟶ ,

July 11, 2003

Dear Linda,

    Last week my family went to the zoo. The animals I liked the best were the monkeys. Here's a picture of one. Do you like monkeys?

Your friend,
Ally

Circle the word that tells where each **comma** is.

The comma in the date comes after the ___.   month   day

The comma in the greeting comes after ___.   Dear   Linda

The comma in the closing comes after ___.   friend   Your

Letter Fix

Read this letter.
Cross out **commas** that are in the wrong places.
Write in **commas** that are missing.
Circle the letters that should be capital letters.

december, 2 2003

dear, lisa

    I am on a ski trip! my family and I drove to Ski-Happy Trails last week.

    I can ski down a big hill. i can ride a rope tow back to the top. it is fun!

        your friend
        Jane,

    Reviewing punctuation and capitalization in a letter

Proper Nouns Use Capitals

A **proper noun** is the name of a specific person, place, or thing. Your name is a **proper noun**.

Every **proper noun** begins with a capital letter.

<u>U</u>nited <u>S</u>tates

<u>J</u>une

Underline the **proper noun** in each sentence that is not written correctly.

The train goes to boston.

maria ran home.

I was born on june 2, 1997.

This man lives in japan.

My cat's name is misty.

ken has a red bike.

Start with a Capital

The first word in a sentence always begins with a capital letter.

This pig is fat.   **The store is open.**

Rewrite each sentence correctly.

cake is yummy.

_____

- - - - - - - - - - - - - - -

_____

use a pen to write.

_____

- - - - - - - - - - - - - - -

_____

bill digs a hole.

_____

- - - - - - - - - - - - - - -

_____

the pin is sharp!

_____

- - - - - - - - - - - - - - -

_____

my fish's name is Goldy.

_____

- - - - - - - - - - - - - - -

_____

Titles Need Capitals

Read the title of this book. Color the capital letters red. Color the other letters yellow. Then color the rest of the book cover.

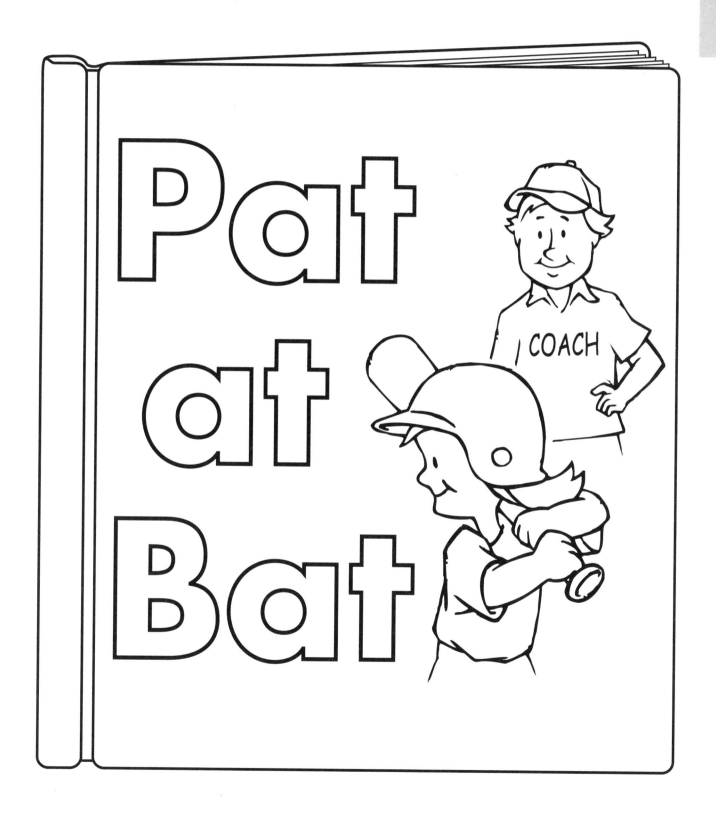

Recognizing capitalization usage in book titles

Book List

Read the list of books. Circle each capital letter.

Oogle and Moogle

How to Talk to a Martian

A Day in the Life of a Slime Monster

Where are capital letters used in book titles? Circle every correct answer.

every word in the title

the first word in the title

the last word in the title

little words like of and the when they are not first or last

names of people and things

verbs

other important words, even when they are not first or last

Recognizing capitalization usage in book titles

Writing Book Titles

When you write about a book, always underline the title.

I read the book <u>Fred Goes to the Zoo</u>.

Think of a book you like. Write its title.
Remember to underline.

_____

- -

_____

Fill in the ◯ by each title that is written correctly.

◯ **<u>Cluck, Cluck, Scoot!</u>**
◯ **<u>cluck, cluck, Scoot!</u>**

◯ **The Very Long Day**
◯ **<u>The Very Long Day</u>**

◯ **<u>My Pal sal</u>**
◯ **<u>My Pal Sal</u>**

Capital Review

Rewrite each sentence correctly.

bob put on a mask.

_____

- - - - - - - - - - - - - - - - -

_____

I like the book A prince's Tale.

_____

- - - - - - - - - - - - - - - - -

_____

the baby horse is cute.

_____

- - - - - - - - - - - - - - - - -

_____

I want to visit alaska.

_____

- - - - - - - - - - - - - - - - -

_____

I go to the store with mom.

_____

- - - - - - - - - - - - - - - - -

_____

Reviewing capitalization

One Word from Two

A **compound word** is made up of two smaller words.

tug + boat = **tugboat**

Find and write two words in each **compound word**.

_____ + _____ = **sunshine**

_____ + _____ = **sailboat**

_____ + _____ = **seashell**

_____ + _____ = **starfish**

_____ + _____ = **swimsuit**

Recognizing compound words

Putting Words Together

A **compound word** is made up of two smaller words.

black + bird = **blackbird**

Write a **compound word** by putting each pair of words together.

cook + book = _____

pan + cake = _____

blue + berry = _____

grape + fruit = _____

high + chair = _____

Forming compound words

Build-a-Word

Write a word from the box to finish each **compound word** below. Then write the **compound word**.

boat	**brush**	**dog**
sand	**scare**	**fire**

_____ + **house** = _____

sail + _____ = _____

camp + _____ = _____

_____ + **box** = _____

_____ + **crow** = _____

tooth + _____ = _____

Compound Word Coloring

Use the code to color the spaces.

compound word = yellow	other word = blue

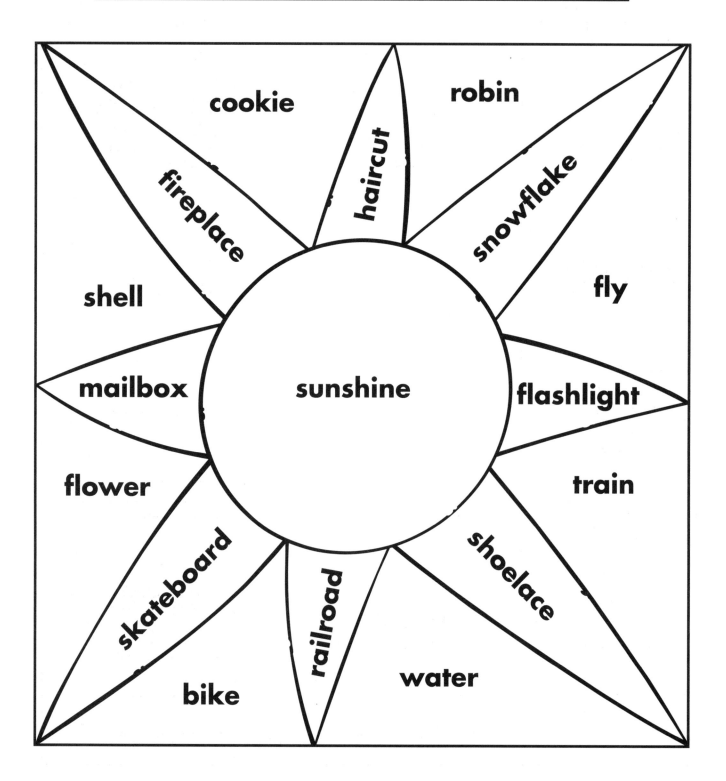

Reviewing compound words

Answer Key

As the child completes the pages in this section, review his or her answers. When you take the time to correct the work and explain mistakes, you're showing your child that you feel learning is important.

page 256

Words that Tell More

Some words tell more about nouns.
They are called **adjectives**.
Adjectives can answer these questions:

What kind?   How many?   What color?
fuzzy bears   **two** bears   **white** bears

Circle the **adjective** in each sentence.

This is (pretty) flower.
It has (two) leaves.

I see (tiny) mice.
I see (three) mice.

She has (long) hair.
She has (big) eyes.

The bus is (big.)
The wheels are (black.)

256   Recognizing adjectives

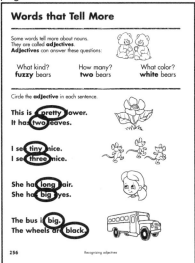

page 257

In the Summertime

Adjectives tell more about nouns.

Write an **adjective** from the box to complete each sentence.

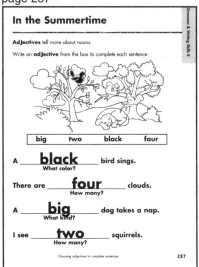

| big | two | black | four |

A ___**black**___ bird sings.
What color?

There are ___**four**___ clouds.
How many?

A ___**big**___ dog takes a nap.
What kind?

I see ___**two**___ squirrels.
How many?

Choosing adjectives to complete sentences   257

page 258

Adjective Search

Circle two **adjectives** in each sentence.

(Two) fish swim under (deep) water.

(Long) eels play by the (old) ship.

Are those (round) shells in the (open) chest?

One (clam) sits on the (smooth) sand.

(Tall) plants grow in the (cool) sea.

(Three) (happy) seahorses play.

258   Identifying adjectives in sentences

page 259

Gardening

Circle the **adjectives** in the box.

| (four) | (pretty) | pea | (proud) |
| rake | (neat) | (two) | are |

Write an **adjective** from the box to complete each sentence.

works in his ___**pretty**___ garden.

He is ___**proud**___ of his garden.

It has ___**two**___ s.

grew ___**four**___ s.

The garden is ___**neat**___ and tidy.

Identifying and using adjectives   259

page 260

Adjective Time

Read the words in each row. Circle the two **adjectives** that tell about the picture.

silly (icy) funny (cold)

loud (wet) (soft) happy

(bright) cool (hot) skinny

Write an **adjective** to complete each sentence.

Answers may vary.

Summer is _____

My friend is _____

Pets are _____

Games are _____

260   Adjective review

page 261

Tell About a Toy

Write the name of a toy you like in the square.
Write an **adjective** that tells about the toy in each circle.

Shape? Feel? Sound?
Size? Color? Smell?

Answers may vary.

Using a graphic organizer to plan a description   261

page 262

Write About a Toy

On page 261 you wrote **adjectives** that tell about your toy.
Use them to write sentences about your toy on the lines below.
Then draw a picture of your toy in the box.

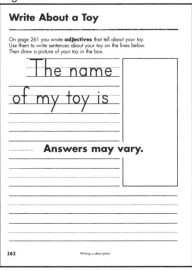

The name of my toy is

Answers may vary.

262   Writing a description

page 263

Telling it All

Some sentences tell something. They are called **statements**.
A **statement** begins with a capital letter and ends with a **period**.

capital letter
The wind is strong**.**
period

Circle the **statement** below.

(Rain fell all day.)
When will the rain stop?

Fill in the ◯ by the **statement** that is written correctly.

◯ today is a cold day.
● Today is a cold day.

● The sky is blue.
◯ the sky is blue.

◯ The children made a snowman
● The children made a snowman.

Recognizing statements and their usage of capital letters and periods   263

page 264

Did You Ask Me?

Some sentences ask something. They are called **questions**.
A **question** begins with a capital letter and ends with a **question mark**.

capital letter   question mark
Who is it**?**

Circle the **questions**.

(Where is my shoe?)
(Will you come with me?)
The cat is in the tree.

Rewrite each **question** correctly.

what is your name
What is your name?

how old are you
How old are you?

where do you live
Where do you live?

264   Recognizing questions and their usage of capital letters and question marks

page 265

Jungle Questions

Color all the **questions marks** hidden in this picture red.
Then color the rest of the picture.

Visual discrimination; identifying question marks   **265**

page 266

Nice Ice

Every **statement** ends with a **period**.
Every **question** ends with a **question mark**.

Add a **period** or **question mark** to the end of each sentence.

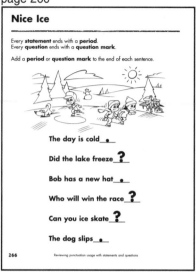

The day is cold __.__

Did the lake freeze __?__

Bob has a new hat __.__

Who will win the race __?__

Can you ice skate __?__

The dog slips __.__

266   Reviewing punctuation usage with statements and questions

page 267

Wow!

A sentence that shows excitement is called an **exclamation**.
Every **exclamation** begins with a capital letter and ends with an **exclamation point**.

capital letter

→ <u>W</u>atch out!

exclamation point

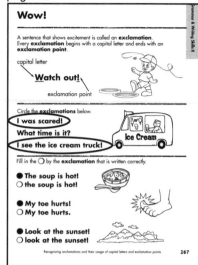

Circle the **exclamations** below.

(I was scared!)
What time is it?
(I see the ice cream truck!)

Fill in the ◯ by the **exclamation** that is written correctly.

● The soup is hot!
◯ the soup is hot!

● My toe hurts!
◯ My toe hurts.

● Look at the sunset!
◯ look at the sunset!

Recognizing exclamations and their usage of capital letters and exclamation points   **267**

page 268

In the Lunch Room

Add a **period**, **question mark**, or **exclamation point** to the end of each sentence.

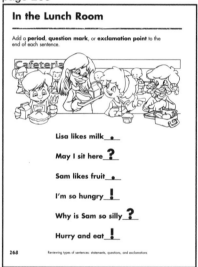

Lisa likes milk __.__

May I sit here __?__

Sam likes fruit __.__

I'm so hungry __!__

Why is Sam so silly __?__

Hurry and eat __!__

268   Reviewing types of sentences: statements, questions, and exclamations

page 269

Please Write!

Read this letter. Look at the names of the different parts of the letter.

Date —→   October 7, 2003

Greeting —→ Dear Grandma,

Body —→   You were right. I do like first
grade. The kids are nice. My teacher
is nice. I work hard, but it is fun.
        Will you come to see me soon?
I hope so. I miss you.

Closing —→   Love,
                    Tommy

Circle the answer.

October 7, 2003	is the	body	(date)
Love,	is the	greeting	(closing)
I miss you.	is part of the	(body)	greeting
Dear Grandma,	is the	(greeting)	closing

Understanding the parts of a letter   **269**

page 270

Return Mail

Read this letter. Circle all the capital letters.

Date —→   ⊙ctober 14, 2003

Greeting —→ ⒹearⓉommy,

Body —→ Ⓘ was happy to get your letter.Ⓘ
am soⒼglad that you like first grade.Ⓘ
will come to see you on
Ⓢunday.Ⓦe can play lots of games
and bake cookies.Ⓘt will be fun!

Closing —→   Ⓛove always,
                    Ⓖrandma

Circle all the answers that are correct.

A capital letter is used at the beginning of:

(the name of a day)   (a person's name)

(the name of the month)   (every sentence)

the year   (the greeting)   (the closing)

270   Understanding capitalization usage in a letter

page 271

Friend to Friend

Read this letter and look for the **commas**.
Circle each **comma** that you find.

comma —→ **,**

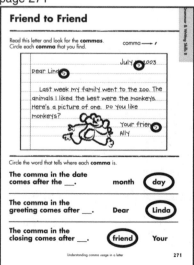

July 7 2003

Dear Linda,

Last week my family went to the zoo. The
animals I liked the best were the monkeys.
Here's a picture of one. Do you like
monkeys?

                    Your friend,
                    Ally

Circle the word that tells where each **comma** is.

The comma in the date
comes after the __.   month   (day)

The comma in the
greeting comes after __.   Dear   (Linda)

The comma in the
closing comes after __.   (friend)   Your

Understanding comma usage in a letter   **271**

page 272

Letter Fix

Read this letter.
Cross out **commas** that are in the wrong places.
Write in **commas** that are missing.
Circle the letters that should be capital letters.

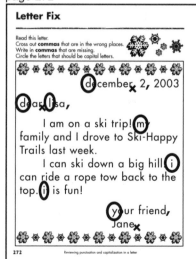

ⓓecember 2, 2003 ✗

ⓓear Ⓛisa,

I am on a ski trip!Ⓜy
family and I drove to Ski-Happy
Trails last week.
        I can ski down a big hill.Ⓘ
can ride a rope tow back to the
top.Ⓘt is fun!

                    Ⓨour friend,
                    Jane✗

272   Reviewing punctuation and capitalization in a letter

page 273

Proper Nouns Use Capitals

A **proper noun** is the name of a specific person, place, or thing.
Your name is a **proper noun**.

Every **proper noun** begins with a capital letter.

<u>United States</u>   <u>June</u>

Underline the **proper noun** in each sentence that is not written correctly.

The train goes to <u>boston</u>.

<u>maria</u> ran home.

I was born on <u>June</u> 2, 1997.

This man lives in <u>Japan</u>.

My cat's name is <u>misty</u>.

<u>ken</u> has a red bike.

Recognizing proper nouns and their use of capitalization   **273**

page 274

Start with a Capital

The first word in a sentence always begins with a capital letter.

This pig is fat.  **The store is open.**

Rewrite each sentence correctly.

cake is yummy.

Cake is yummy.

use a pen to write.

Use a pen to write.

bill digs a hole.

Bill digs a hole.

the pin is sharp!

The pin is sharp!

my fish's name is goldy.

My fish's name is Goldy.

274   Using a capital letter at the beginning of a sentence

page 275

Titles Need Capitals

Read the title of this book. Color the capital letters red. Color the other letters yellow. Then color the rest of the book cover.

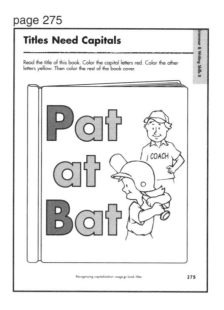

275   Recognizing capitalization usage in book titles

page 276

Book List

Read the list of books. Circle each capital letter.

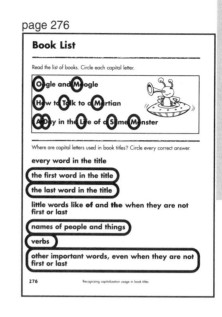

Ⓞgle and Ⓜⓞⓞgle

Ⓗⓞw to Ⓣⓐlk to ⓐ Ⓜartian

Ⓐ Ⓓⓐy in the Ⓛⓘⓕe of ⓐ Ⓢⓛⓘⓜe Ⓜⓞnster

Where are capital letters used in book titles? Circle every correct answer.

every word in the title

(the first word in the title)

(the last word in the title)

little words like **of** and **the** when they are not first or last

(names of people and things)

(verbs)

(other important words, even when they are not first or last)

276   Recognizing capitalization usage in book titles

page 277

Writing Book Titles

When you write about a book, always underline the title.

I read the book <u>Fred Goes to the Zoo</u>.

Think of a book you like. Write its title. Remember to underline.

- - - - - **Answers may vary.** - - - - -

Fill in the ◯ by each title that is written correctly.

● **Cluck, Cluck, Scoot!**
◯ <u>cluck, cluck, Scoot!</u>

◯ The Very Long Day
● <u>The Very Long Day</u>

◯ <u>My Pal sal</u>
● <u>My Pal Sal</u>

277   Understanding the mechanics of writing a book title: underscoring and capitalization

page 278

Capital Review

Rewrite each sentence correctly.

bob put on a mask.

Bob put on a mask.

I like the book A prince's Tale.

I like the book <u>A Prince's Tale</u>.

the baby horse is cute.

The baby horse is cute.

I want to visit alaska.

I want to visit Alaska.

I go to the store with mom.

I go to the store with Mom.

278   Reviewing capitalization

page 279

One Word from Two

A **compound word** is made up of two smaller words.

tug + boat = **tugboat**

Find and write two words in each **compound word**.

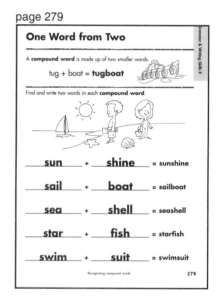

sun + **shine** = sunshine

sail + **boat** = sailboat

sea + **shell** = seashell

star + **fish** = starfish

swim + **suit** = swimsuit

279   Recognizing compound words

page 280

Putting Words Together

A **compound word** is made up of two smaller words.

black + bird = **blackbird**

Write a **compound word** by putting each pair of words together.

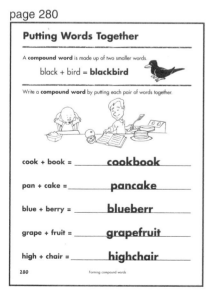

cook + book = **cookbook**

pan + cake = **pancake**

blue + berry = **blueberr**

grape + fruit = **grapefruit**

high + chair = **highchair**

280   Forming compound words

page 281

Build-a-Word

Write a word from the box to finish each **compound word** below. Then write the **compound word**.

| boat | brush | dog |
| sand | scare | fire |

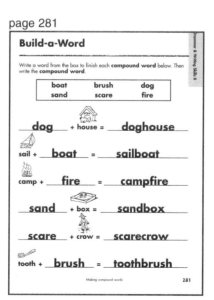

dog + house = **doghouse**

sail + **boat** = **sailboat**

camp + **fire** = **campfire**

sand + box = **sandbox**

scare + crow = **scarecrow**

tooth + **brush** = **toothbrush**

281   Making compound words

page 282

Compound Word Coloring

Use the code to color the spaces.

| compound word = yellow | other word = blue |

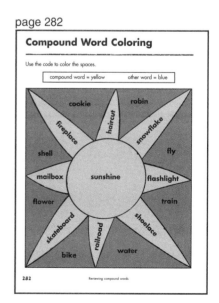

282   Reviewing compound words

Under the Sea

Read each color word and then rewrite it.
Use the number next to each color word to color the picture.

red   **1**

_____

- - - - - - - - - - -

_____

green   **2**

_____

- - - - - - - - - - -

_____

blue   **3**

_____

- - - - - - - - - - -

_____

yellow   **4**

_____

- - - - - - - - - - -

_____

     Recognizing and writing color words

A Colorful House

Read each color word and then rewrite it.
Use the number next to each color word to color the picture.

orange   **1**

_____

- - - - - - - - - - - - - - -

_____

brown   **2**

_____

- - - - - - - - - - - - - - -

_____

black   **3**

_____

- - - - - - - - - - - - - - -

_____

purple   **4**

_____

- - - - - - - - - - - - - - -

_____

Reading Comprehension

Words to Know—People

Read the word under each picture.

girl    **boy**    **mother**    **father**

Write the name of each picture.

_____

_ _ _ _ _ _ _ _ _

_____

_____

_ _ _ _ _ _ _ _ _

_____

_____

_ _ _ _ _ _ _ _ _

_____

_____

_ _ _ _ _ _ _ _ _

_____

Reading and writing commonly used nouns: people

Words to Know—Animals

Read the word under each picture.

cat

dog

fish

bird

Write one of the words above to complete each sentence.

My _____ **chews bones.**

My _____ **has a long tail.**

My _____ **sings a song.**

My _____ **swims in water.**

Reading and writing commonly used nouns: animals

Words to Know—School Tools

Read the word under each picture.

pencil   **paper**   **crayon**   **scissors**

Write the name of each picture.

_____   _____
- - - - - - - - - - - -   - - - - - - - - - - - -
_____   _____

_____   _____
- - - - - - - - - - - -   - - - - - - - - - - - -
_____   _____

Words to Know—Directions

Read the word under each picture.

cut

color

write

draw

1. What do we cut paper with? Draw its picture in Box 1.
2. Color the bird in Box 2.
3. Write **OK** in Box 3.
4. Draw a 🌼 in Box 4.

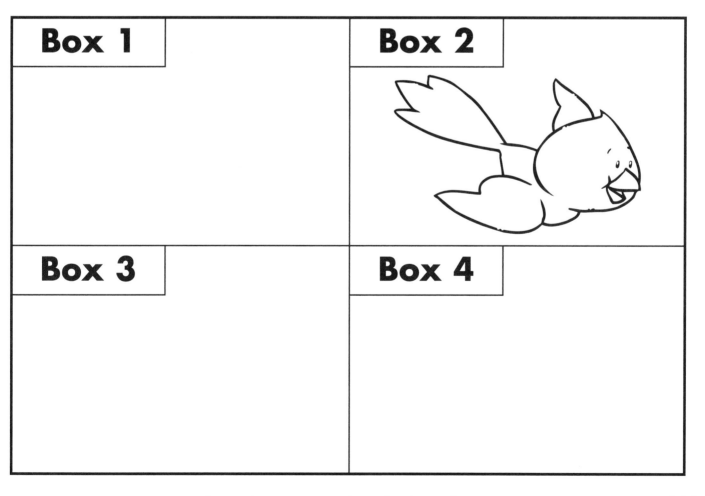

Box 1

Box 2

Box 3

Box 4

Words To Know Review

Write two words from the box to complete each sentence.

mother	fish	bird	cut	scissors
boy	father	write	draw	pencil

My _____ likes to _____.

Use a  _____ to _____.

My _____ feeds our _____.

I will _____ with _____.

The _____ sees a _____.

Reviewing commonly used nouns and verbs

Which House is Mine?

Each girl is saying something. The missing words are on her house.
Write the correct words to complete the sentences.

My cat is _____.

She has a pink _____.

nose
cute

I _____ ice cream.

It is good with _____.

cake
like

Dad will _____ home soon.

Then we will _____.

play
be

Goldilocks and the Three Bears, Part 1

Fill in the missing words in the story and then read it aloud.

Mother Bear

Goldilocks

 **Father Bear**

 **Baby Bear**

The _____ **(had, hid)** a little

_____ **(in, on)** the woods.

One day _____ **(Mother, mixer)** Bear

said, "I will _____ **(fax, fix)** a ⬭ for you."

But the ⬭ was too _____ **(hit, hot)**. So the

_____ **(went, want)** for a walk.

A little _____ **(green, girl)** named Goldilocks

was _____ **(last, lost)** in the woods. Goldilocks

saw the 🏠 and went _____ **(in, on)**.

Reading a story and supplying missing words

Goldilocks and the Three Bears, Part 2

Goldilocks _____ (**sat, sot**) in Baby Bear's

_____. She was too _____ (**bag, big**)

for the _____ and _____ (**at, it**) broke.

Goldilocks saw the _____ that was _____

(**sat, set**) out to cool. She ate _____ (**all, ill**) of

Baby Bear's _____ ! Then she laid _____

(**down, duck**) on Baby Bear's _____ (**bad, bed**).

The _____ came _____ (**back, buck**).

They saw the _____ and the _____ . Baby Bear was

_____ (**sad, sod**). His _____ (**dad, did**)

was _____ (**mud, mad**).

Then the _____ saw Goldilocks

_____ (**and, end**) she saw them. Goldilocks

jumped _____ (**up, us**) and ran away—

_____ (**fast, fist**)!

The _____ (**End, And**)!

Reading Comprehension

Real or Not?

A story that tells about things that could really happen is called **realistic**. A story that tells about things that could not happen and are make-believe is called a **fantasy**.

Look at each picture. If it shows something happening that could be real, circle **R** for **realistic**. If it shows something happening that is only make-believe, circle **F** for **fantasy**. Then color the pictures.

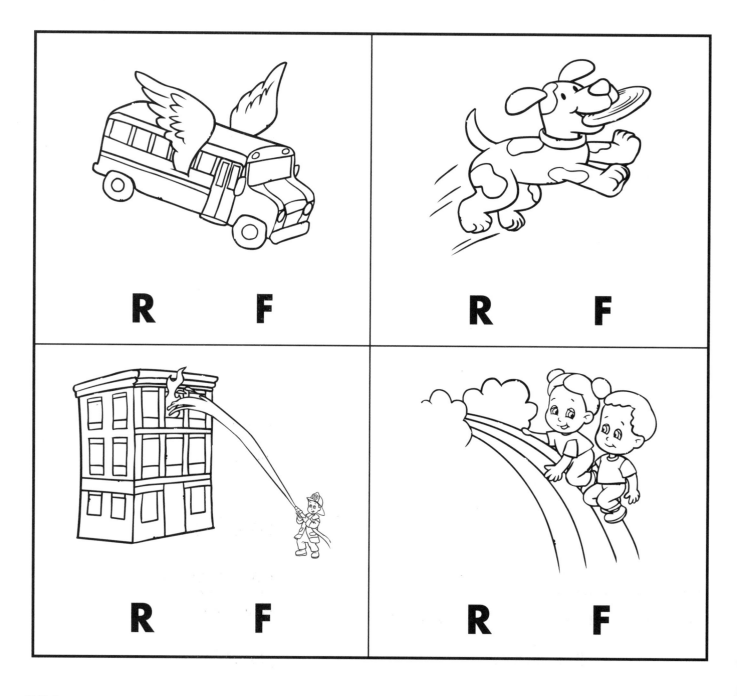

R   F

R   F

R   F

R   F

Discriminating between reality and fantasy

Believe It or Not!

The picture below shows the beginning of a story. Color it.

Think about how you would finish the story and draw three more pictures to show what would happen next.

You can make your story **realistic** or you can make it a **fantasy**.

Which kind of story did you make? Circle one.

realistic   **fantasy**

Order Please!

The pictures in each row tell a story, but they are out of order.
Put them in order by numbering them **1**, **2**, and **3**.
Then color the pictures.

Understanding story sequence

A Surprise Box

Read each sentence and draw a line to its matching picture.
Then number the **events** in order from **1** to **4**.

☐ **Kate finds a box.**

☐ **Kate puts the hat on.**

☐ **Kate opens the box.**

☐ **Kate sees a hat in the box.**

Understanding story sequence

That's the Idea!

The **main idea** of a story is its most important idea.

Each row of pictures tells a story. Underline the sentence that tells the **main idea** of each story.

The party was fun.   **Jake wore a party hat.**

No one had fun at the party.   **The cake was big.**

The kittens were white.   **Sue gave away three kittens.**

The kittens were small.   **Sue kept three kittens.**

Identifying the main idea of a story told in pictures

What Does Not Belong?

The pictures below tell more about a **main idea**.
Cross out the picture that does not belong in each group.

Identifying pictures that do not relate to the main idea

What's the Main Idea?

The **main idea** is the most important idea.

Circle the **main idea** of each picture.

The giant is nice.

The giant eats a lot.

The clown is sad.

The clown is funny.

We have lots of fruit.

We have no fruit.

My friend moved away.

My friend has short hair.

Choosing the Main Idea

Read each story. Circle the sentence that tells the **main idea**.

It is raining. Ann puts on boots. She puts on a raincoat. She puts on a hat. Now she is ready.

Ann dresses for a rainy day.

Ann takes a long time to dress.

The house is old. It needs new paint. The windows are broken. The door is loose. The roof has holes.

The house is old but nice.

The old house needs to be fixed.

Fun on the Farm

Look closely at the picture and then circle the answer to each question.

Which animal is asleep?	**cow** **cat**
Where is the nest?	**on a branch** **in the barn**
How many eggs are in the nest?	**two** **four**
Where do flowers grow?	**by the fence** **by the barn**
Where is the bird?	**on the roof** **in the air**
What is by the fence?	**dog** **cow**

Recalling picture details

A Beautiful Day

Look closely at the picture and then circle the answer to each question.

What is in the tree?	**bird** **cat**
Who is on the slide?	**girl** **boy**
What is the boy wearing?	**a jacket** **a hat**
Who has a balloon?	**boy** **mother**
Where is the bench?	**by a tree** **by a pond**
Who is on the bench?	**mother** **girl**

Recalling picture details

Story Memory

Read the story.

Jim has three dogs. The names of the dogs are Tip, Jed and Bud.

Tip likes meat. Jed likes bones. Bud likes to play ball.

Jim gives Tip meat. He gives Jed a bone. He plays ball with Bud.

The dogs love Jim. Jim loves his dogs.

Circle the answer to each question.

What does Bud like to do?

play ball	eat meat

What does Jim give Jed?

a bone	a ball

The names of the dogs are Jed, Bud and _____ .

Jim	Tip

Recalling details in a story

Details, Details

A **detail** is a fact that tells more about the **main idea**.

Look for **details** as you read this short story.

> **This is my cat, Tiger. He has soft fur. He has stripes. He has a long tail. He sleeps on my bed at night. He purrs in my ear to wake me up. He is a good friend.**

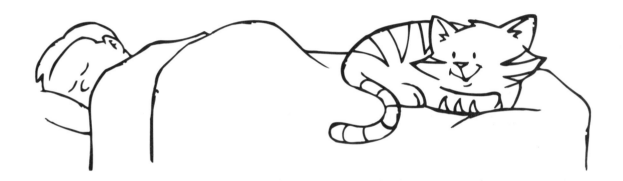

Circle the answers.

What is the name of the cat?	**Tiger** **Kitty**
What is his fur like?	**rough** **soft**
What is his tail like?	**long** **short**
Where does he sleep?	**on the bed** **in a box**

Using Picture Clues

Use the picture clues to guess what is happening.
Circle the guess that fits the clues.

The boy won a race.

The boy lost a race.

The girl wants to eat.

The girl does not want to eat.

It is quiet.

There is a loud noise.

Sam ate some jelly.

Sam did not eat jelly.

Making inferences using visual clues

Picture Detective

Use the picture clues to guess what is happening.
Circle the guess that fits the clues.

This girl likes carrots.

This girl does not like carrots.

Today is windy.

There is no wind today.

The bag is heavy.

The bag is light.

The team just lost the game.

The team just won the game.

Making inferences using visual clues

Use Your Head

First look at the picture on the left of each row. Then look at the picture on the right. Circle the sentence that tells what most likely happened between the pictures.

The girl did not hit the ball.

The girl hit the ball into the window.

The sun came out.

It got colder.

The branch broke off.

The boy cut the branch off.

Drawing conclusions

A Day At School

Look at the picture and read about what is happening.

**The boys and girls are at school.
Nell cuts paper. Ted colors with a crayon.
Ben writes with a pencil. Jill draws a fish.**

Now that you have looked at the picture and read about it, circle all the answers you think are true.

**The boys and girls
work well in school.**

**The boys and girls
do not work hard.**

**The boys and girls
are sad.**

**The boys and girls
are happy.**

**The teacher is
proud of them.**

**The teacher is not
proud of them.**

What Comes Next?

It is fun to guess what will happen next in a story. To guess well, you need to think about all the clues.

These pictures tell part of a story. Use the picture clues to guess what will happen next.

Draw a picture of what you guessed.

Predicting outcomes

What Will Happen Next?

Read this part of a story. Think about what might happen next.

The puppy has been told many times not to sit on the new chair. But one day he is home alone. He wants to take a nap. The chair looks so soft.

Draw a picture of what you think will happen next.

Write about what you think will happen next.

_____

_____

_____

_____

_____

Why Did This Happen?

A **cause** is the reason why something happens.
An **effect** is what happens.

 **Cause:** ⟶ **Effect:**
Jenny gave her flower water.   The flower grew tall and strong.

Draw a line to match each **cause** with its **effect**.

CAUSE

EFFECT

 Bear was hungry.

He got a sunburn.

 **Bear was tired.**

He ate a big meal.

 **Bear sat in the sun.**

He got lost.

 **Bear went far away.**

He went to bed.

Understanding cause and effect

Be a Detective!

Look at the picture. Use the clues to discover **causes** and **effects**.

Draw a line between each **effect** and its **cause**.

EFFECT

The boy runs.

The girl is mad.

The baby yawns.

The man smiles.

CAUSE

She is sleepy.

He is getting a present.

She fell into the pond.

He is being chased by bees.

Understanding cause and effect

Answer Key

As the child completes the pages in this section, review his or her answers. When you take the time to correct the work and explain mistakes, you're showing your child that you feel learning is important.

page 286

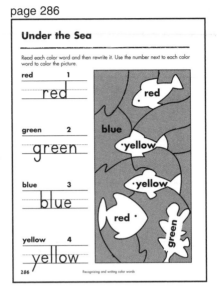

page 287

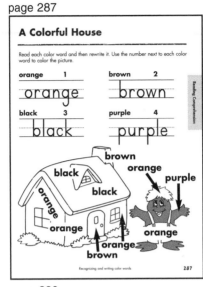

page 288

page 289

page 290

page 291

page 292

page 293

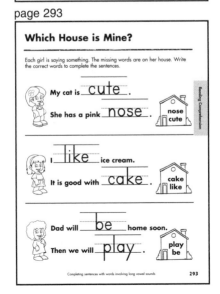

page 294

page 295

Goldilocks and the Three Bears, Part 2

Goldilocks **sat** (sat, sot) in Baby Bear's 🪑. She was too **big** (bag, big) for the 🪑 and **it** (at, it) broke.

Goldilocks saw the 🥣 that was **set** (sat, set) out to cool. She ate **all** (all, ill) of Baby Bear's 🥣! Then she laid **down** (down, duck) on Baby Bear's **bed** (bad, bed).

The 🐻🐻 came **back** (back, buck). They saw the 🪑 and the 🥣. Baby Bear was **sad** (sad, sod). His **dad** (dad, did) was **mad** (mud, mad).

Then the 🐻🐻 saw Goldilocks **and** (and, end) she saw them. Goldilocks jumped **up** (up, us) and ran away— **fast** (fast, fist)!

The **End** (End, And)!

Reading a story and supplying missing words — 295

page 296

Real or Not?

A story that tells about things that could really happen is called **realistic**. A story that tells about things that could not happen and are make-believe is called a **fantasy**.

Look at each picture. If it shows something happening that could be real, circle **R** for **realistic**. If it shows something happening that is only make-believe, circle **F** for **fantasy**. Then color the pictures.

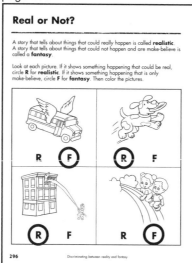

296 — Discriminating between reality and fantasy

page 297

Believe It or Not!

The picture below shows the beginning of a story. Color it.

Think about how you would finish the story and draw three more pictures to show what would happen next.

You can make your story **realistic** or you can make it a **fantasy**.

Answers may vary.

Which kind of story did you make? Circle one.

Answers may vary.

Discriminating between reality and fantasy — 297

page 298

Order Please!

The pictures in each row tell a story, but they are out of order. Put them in order by numbering them **1**, **2**, and **3**. Then color the pictures.

298 — Understanding story sequence

page 299

Out of Order

These pictures tell a story, but they are out of order. Number them from **1** to **6** to show the correct order. Then color the pictures and tell the story aloud.

Understanding story sequence — 299

page 300

A Walk in the Woods

Read the story.

Dan took a walk in the woods. First he saw a bird. Then he saw a deer. Next he saw a bunny. Then Dan saw a skunk, and he ran away!

The pictures show the **events** in the story. The **events** are the things that happen in the story. Number the **events** in order from **1** to **4**. Then color the pictures.

300 — Understanding story sequence

page 301

A Surprise Box

Read each sentence and draw a line to its matching picture. Then number the **events** in order from **1** to **4**.

1 Kate finds a box.

4 Kate puts the hat on.

2 Kate opens the box.

3 Kate sees a hat in the box.

Understanding story sequence — 301

page 302

That's the Idea!

The **main idea** of a story is its most important idea.

Each row of pictures tells a story. Underline the sentence that tells the **main idea** of each story.

The party was fun.   Jake wore a party hat.

No one had fun at the party.   The cake was big.

The kittens were white.   Sue gave away three kittens.

The kittens were small.   Sue kept three kittens.

302 — Identifying the main idea of a story told in pictures

page 303

What Does Not Belong?

The pictures below tell more about a **main idea**. Cross out the picture that does not belong in each group.

Identifying pictures that do not relate to the main idea — 303

Reading Comprehension

page 304

What's the Main Idea?

The **main idea** is the most important idea.

Circle the main idea of each picture.

- The giant is nice.
- **The giant eats a lot.**

- **The clown is sad.**
- The clown is funny.

- **We have lots of fruit.**
- We have no fruit.

- **My friend moved away.**
- My friend has short hair.

page 305

Choosing the Main Idea

Read each story. Circle the sentence that tells the **main idea**.

It is raining. Ann puts on boots. She puts on a raincoat. She puts on a hat. Now she is ready.

- **Ann dresses for a rainy day.**
- Ann takes a long time to dress.

The house is old. It needs new paint. The windows are broken. The door is loose. The roof has holes.

- The house is old but nice.
- **The old house needs to be fixed.**

page 306

Fun on the Farm

Look closely at the picture and then circle the answer to each question.

- Which animal is asleep? — cow / **cat**
- Where is the nest? — **on a branch** / in the barn
- How many eggs are in the nest? — two / **four**
- Where do flowers grow? — by the fence / **by the barn**
- Where is the bird? — on the roof / **in the air**
- What is by the fence? — dog / **cow**

page 307

A Beautiful Day

Look closely at the picture and then circle the answer to each question.

- What is in the tree? — **bird** / cat
- Who is on the slide? — **girl** / boy
- What is the boy wearing? — **a jacket** / a hat
- Who has a balloon? — **boy** / mother
- Where is the bench? — **by a tree** / by a pond
- Who is on the bench? — **mother** / girl

page 308

Story Memory

Read the story.

Jim has three dogs. The names of the dogs are Tip, Jed and Bud. Tip likes meat. Jed likes bones. Bud likes to play ball. Jim gives Tip meat. He gives Jed a bone. He plays ball with Bud. The dogs love Jim. Jim loves his dogs.

Circle the answer to each question.

What does Bud like to do? — **play ball** / eat meat

What does Jim give Jed? — **a bone** / a ball

The names of the dogs are Jed, Bud and _____. — Jim / **Tip**

page 309

Details, Details

A **detail** is a fact that tells more about the **main idea**.

Look for **details** as you read this short story.

This is my cat, Tiger. He has soft fur. He has stripes. He has a long tail. He sleeps on my bed at night. He purrs in my ear to wake me up. He is a good friend.

Circle the answers.

- What is the name of the cat? — **Tiger** / Kitty
- What is his fur like? — rough / **soft**
- What is his tail like? — **long** / short
- Where does he sleep? — **on the bed** / in a box

page 310

Using Picture Clues

Use the picture clues to guess what is happening. Circle the guess that fits the clues.

- **The boy won a race.**
- The boy lost a race.

- **The girl wants to eat.**
- The girl does not want to eat.

- It is quiet.
- **There is a loud noise.**

- **Sam ate some Jelly.**
- Sam did not eat Jelly.

page 311

Picture Detective

Use the picture clues to guess what is happening. Circle the guess that fits the clues.

- This girl likes carrots.
- **This girl does not like carrots.**

- **Today is windy.**
- There is no wind today.

- **The bag is heavy.**
- The bag is light.

- The team just lost the game.
- **The team just won the game.**

page 314: Answers may vary.

page 315: Answers may vary.

page 312

Use Your Head

First look at the picture on the left of each row. Then look at the picture on the right. Circle the sentence that tells what most likely happened between the pictures.

- The girl did not hit the ball.
- **The girl hit the ball into the window.**

- **The sun came out.**
- It got colder.

- **The branch broke off.**
- The boy cut the branch off.

page 313

A Day At School

Look at the picture and read about what is happening.

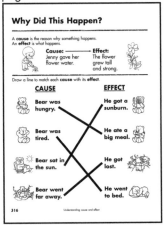

The boys and girls are at school. Nell cuts paper. Ted colors with a crayon. Ben writes with a pencil. Jill draws a fish.

Now that you have looked at the picture and read about it, circle all the answers you think are true.

- **The boys and girls work well in school.**
- The boys and girls do not work hard.
- The boys and girls are sad.
- **The boys and girls are happy.**
- **The teacher is proud of them.**
- The teacher is not proud of them.

page 316

Why Did This Happen?

A **cause** is the reason why something happens. An **effect** is what happens.

Cause: Jenny gave her flower water. → Effect: The flower grew tall and strong.

Draw a line to match each **cause** with its **effect**.

CAUSE	EFFECT
Bear was hungry.	He got a sunburn.
Bear was tired.	He ate a big meal.
Bear sat in the sun.	He got lost.
Bear went far away.	He went to bed.

page 317

Be a Detective!

Look at the picture. Use the clues to discover **causes** and **effects**.

Draw a line between each **effect** and its **cause**.

EFFECT	CAUSE
The boy runs.	She is sleepy.
The girl is mad.	He is getting a present.
The baby yawns.	She fell into the pond.
The man smiles.	He is being chased by bees.